Beyond
PROVIDER
Dominance

Fiona Hastings

Published by the King's Fund
2 Palace Court
London W2

Tel: 071-727 0581

ISBN 1 85717 053 9

A CIP catalogue record for this book is available from the British Library

Distributed by Bournemouth English Book Centre (BEBC)
PO Box 1496
Poole
Dorset
BH12 3YD

Illustration and text taken from *Alice's Adventures in Wonderland and Through the Looking Glass* by Lewis Carroll, illustration by Sir John Tenniel, edition published 1974 by Book Club Associates, by arrangement with Oxford University Press. Introduction, notes, bibliography and chronology copyright Oxford University Press 1974. Printed by permission of Oxford University Press.

CONTENTS

ACKNOWLEDGEMENTS

To Heraclitus for recognising the importance of transition and change in human affairs.

To Len Schaeffer of Blue Cross for hospitality and inspiration during the Conference.

To all conference delegates for their willingness to think, talk and listen.

To King's Fund College colleagues for support and advice, Marie-Louise for editing help and Geneve Fuller for patient secretarial support.

And to a thought: 'death is a failure of the health care delivery system' – for reminding us of the limits of human endeavour.

CONTRIBUTORS

Robert J Maxwell	Chief Executive and Secretary, King Edward's Hospital Fund for London
Fiona M Hastings	Fellow, King's Fund College
Gordon Best	Part time Fellow and former Director, King's Fund College
Leonard Schaeffer	President and Chief Executive Officer, Blue Cross of California
David Knowles	Fellow, King's Fund College and former District General Manager, Riverside, London, United Kingdom
Steven R Leeder	Director, Department of Community Medicine, University of Sydney, Australia
Ed Connors	President, Mercy Health Services, Michigan, United States
Marie Fortier	Director General, Health Services Directorate, Department of National Health & Welfare, Canada
Ken Fyke	President and Chief Executive Officer, Greater Victoria Hospital, Victoria, British Columbia, Canada
Jennifer Alexander	General Superintendent, Westmead Hospital, New South Wales, Australia
Karen Poutasi	General Manager, Wellington Area Health Board, Wellington, New Zealand
Jo Boufford	Director, King's Fund College, United Kingdom
Christine Hancock	General Secretary, Royal College of Nursing, United Kingdom
Sandy Bradbrook	District General Manager, Wigan, United Kingdom
Dan Longo	President, The Hospital Research and Educational Trust, Chicago, United States
Frank Burns	Chief Executive, Arrowe Park Hospital, Merseyside
Steve Herbert	President, Royal Victoria Hospital, Montreal, Canada
Don Schurman	President, University of Alberta Hospitals, Edmonton, Alberta, Canada
Fred Alley	President and Chief Executive Officer, Brooklyn-Caledonian Hospital, United States
Rick Norling	President and Chief Executive Officer, Fairview Hospital, Minniapolis/St Paul, United States
Diana Horvath	Director of Health Services, Eastern Sydney Area Health Service, New South Wales, Australia
John Morris	Chief Executive Officer, Peter McCallum Cancer Institute, Melbourne, Australia
Glen Garlick	General Manager, Wackato Area Health Board, New Zealand

PREFACE

MANAGING THE CHANGING RELATIONSHIP BETWEEN PAYERS, PROVIDERS AND PATIENTS: AN INTRODUCTION TO THE THEME

ROBERT J. MAXWELL

The differences among health systems are very striking. One can go on collecting variations in their structures and financing as endlessly as postage stamps. Nevertheless, the fundamental issues of health, disease and handicap, and of medical care, are the same. So it is, perhaps, not surprising that people in positions of leadership in different health systems should find that they have concerns in common and that they benefit from listening to one another. That is the foundation on which a long, and remarkably successful, series of King's Fund's International Seminars has been built. It is not so much that people find through these exchanges any readymade solutions to their problems, but that they learn from other people's perceptions and approaches, and that they go away with renewed insight and courage.

This book stems from one such seminar, mediated through the reflections of one of the participants, Fiona Hastings. She has not edited the papers in the normal sense, but has used them, along with other material, to make a book that is distinctively her own. Some of the papers are included more or less as originally written. Others appear only in very brief excerpts, where they illustrate a point in her broader argument.

The starting point

The starting point for the seminar was the purchaser/provider split, which is familiar in insurance-based systems of health care, but which struck the National Health Service with the force of an ideological tornado in 1990. Immediate reactions in the medical and nursing professions were deeply hostile, and the public was, to say the least, sceptical. The purchaser/provider split, however, appeared to me to offer a way of distancing resource allocation from the more or less automatic perpetuation of existing services and institutions, and instead rooting it in a community's health care needs. It might make the whole business of reconciling (limited) budgets and (unlimited) objectives less hidden and more open to public understanding. And – so its proponents claimed – it should be possible to reward efficient providers: money would follow the patient.

Whatever one's views about the merits and potential of the purchaser/provider split – and my own view at that stage was that we must try it out and if it did not work change it – it was not a sufficient description of a health care system. After all, where was the patient in all this? So, in thinking about the seminar, we had in mind the following triangle:

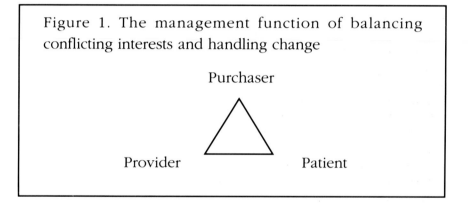

Figure 1. The management function of balancing conflicting interests and handling change

Purchaser

Provider   Patient

What we wanted to explore was the changing relationships between payers and providers, and how these changing relationships affect patients. Not in Britain alone, but in all the countries with which we were concerned (the United States, Canada, Australia, New Zealand and the UK), the financial control function had become stronger in the 1980s. The providers – the professions and institutions – are being challenged with new intensity to justify their decisions. The tensions between payers and providers have increased. The way that these tensions are managed in the 1990s will be an increasingly important determinant of who gets what care, how good it is, and how much it costs.

In every system, lip service is paid to the importance of patients. In the past, it was often good enough simply to take the line that patients presented themselves and providers could best judge what care was needed and how to provide it. Today, however, it is increasingly common for a paying or purchasing agent to act, in effect, as a patient 'advocate'. In these circumstances, the payer will often pursue policies designed to ensure that patients gain ready access to the care they require; that the care is delivered in a sensitive and convenient manner; and that costs are kept within reasonable bounds. In short, the payer may act so as to ensure that the patient is treated as a valued 'customer'. But that does not mean the interests of payer and patient are identical. After all, the payer is at risk financially and may at times impede the patient's access to services.

This is, of course, an over-simple sketch of some of the many changes which are presently in train in many countries. Key themes suggested by Figure 1 include the following:

- Balancing different perceptions of value. For example, how do payers weigh up cost savings against service or clinical quality? How do providers see this equation? Are patients simply pawns in a game between the two main players? How can their interests be best protected?

- How do the different players (that is, payer, provider or patient) deal with the changing demands of the others?

- How can the tensions between payers, providers and patients be managed so as to change the health system for the better? For example, how can payers use their financial 'leverage ' to bring about changes in provider behaviour?

- What needs to be done to protect the positive aspects of professional autonomy, and the need for professional satisfaction, from increasing payer control?

- How can payers and providers design 'win/win' situations that are in the interests of patients?

- What happens if the third 'P' is viewed as the community rather than as the individual patient? Does this change the payer's role and responsibilities? If so, how?

- What is the political dimension in all this? For example, what changes when the government is the payer, 'the patient advocate', or the provider?

- What are the roles and responsibilities of top managers in payer and provider organisations? What would be the characteristics of responsible and effective organisational (or business) strategies for payers and providers?

The seminar and its conclusions

What had seemed beforehand rather a bold title – 'Beyond Provider Dominance' – came to seem correct in the sense that there is unlikely to be any widespread return to a situation in which providers are not challenged by patients to justify their actions, either by the payers, or by the Government. For better or for worse (and it is mainly better) we have moved on from there.

After listening to a week's discussion, I was inclined to revise Figure 1 from a triangle to a star as shown in Figure 2.

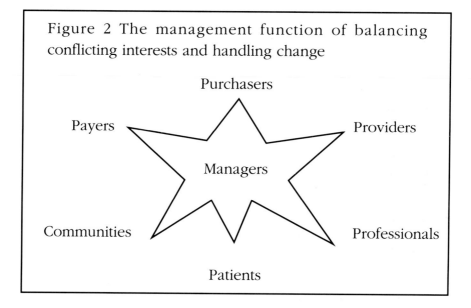

Figure 2 The management function of balancing conflicting interests and handling change

Purchasers

Payers

Providers

Managers

Communities

Professionals

Patients

(Arguably, even then 'provider' needs to be further broken down into the professions on the one hand, and the institutions on the other.) Although the resulting figure is more complex, the complexity that it recognises is real. For example, the interests of the individual patient and of the community at large do not always, nor necessarily, coincide.

Other lessons taken away were some sharp views about where each system ought to go next in its development for the 1990s. For example:

● Australia has to sort out the relative responsibilities of the Federal and State governments in relation to health before much progress can be made in the management of the system.

- Canada has had considerable stability in its health systems since the mid 1970s. The public is largely content and so are the doctors. The hospitals believe that their budgets have been pared unreasonably and that standards cannot be maintained. Who is right? Unusually among health systems, the Canadian system may actually need destabilising in order to raise and tackle some necessary questions about where it should be heading.

- New Zealand at that time (late 1990) seemed to have reacted against the sharp ideological separation of the purchaser/provider split, which was far more cogently argued in the Gibbs report of 1988 than in the British Government's Review of the NHS in 1988/89. Instead, New Zealand was opting for quite a centralised, dirigiste emphasis on the duty of its new health boards to deliver health gain. (Since then there has been a change of government in New Zealand and a return to the rhetoric of markets.)

- The UK, which was at that time feeling bludgeoned by the changes introduced by the 1990 NHS and Community Care Act, needed to get out of its hair-shirt mode and its preoccupation with NHS structures and systems, and get on with the business of health care and health.

- The United States had – and still has – two besetting problems which it seemed totally unable to tackle. One was its inability to curb health care expenditures. The other is the lack of any systematic provision for some 35 million uninsured Americans – a position without parallel in any other developed country.

In terms of overall messages, broader than any one country, I would select five as follow.

1. The question at a health systems level of 'What is all this for?'

The mission of the individual clinician may be very clear – though it too can be complex in situations where survival at all costs is not the sole issue. At the institutional level, mission needs to be about more than institutional aggrandisement and survival – hence it really is about more complex issues than in the commercial field. But it is at the systems level that mission and shared vision are at their most tantalising and elusive. Is it about high quality health care, or equity, or affordability, or some mixture of all these? Is it about the health of the nation? At all events, we need

---

Gibbs, A (Chair). 'Unshackling the Hospitals' Government paper, Wellington, New Zealand. (ISBN 0-477-04520-0)

rather more clarity about that in most systems for (as the Cheshire Cat said to Alice), 'If you don't know where you want to go, it doesn't much matter which way you go, does it?'. In terms of the structure of the present book, this is the first 'F' – focus – that Fiona Hastings selects.

2. How can we empower patients and communities?

It may be a good thing that the health professions and the institutions in which they work should be more accountable to the payers than they have been in the past. But it is essential that this should not be seen simply as a struggle between providers and payers, with the patients and the public as pawns in the game. It is, after all, they who stand to gain or lose most from the standard of services provided and they from whom, in the end, the money comes. The hard choices about risk and net benefit are, at root, personal choices where nobody should act without involving the patient in the choices, to the extent that the patient wants to be involved. Similarly, at the community level, choices of priority within resource limits are not simply technical matters for payers and providers to decide between them: they are public policy choices. We have a long way to go before the third P of the triangle or the two (public and patient) points of the star are anything like a match for the payers and providers in most of our health systems.

3. Granted that health care needs and medical technology will continue to grow faster than GDP, how are the uncomfortable problems of doing more for the same money to be handled?

Part of the answer has to lie in steadily increasing efficiency year by year – not as easy in service industries as in manufacturing but both possible and necessary. Part also has to lie with much greater discrimination in choosing what is worth doing, for example in the introduction of new technologies (and the withdrawal of old ones) and in interventions that are driven more by habit and good intent than by the interests of the patient. My suspicion, however, is that neither of these types of measures will be enough – that we also have to face up to questions of public priority within resource constraints, in ways that few of our systems yet do. This is, of course, a topic for a whole new book. It also perhaps fits under Fiona's 'F' for flexibility.

4. Assuming that management has a key role in balancing the tensions inherent in the triangle (Figure 1) or the star (Figure 2), can it use these tensions constructively to improve health care and to promote health?

It is pretty obvious that there is a major political element (with both a small 'p' and a large 'P') to the public management of health systems. Political sensitivity is essential for survival at the top, and the knack of building alliances (part of Fiona Hastings' 'F' for friendliness) is crucial to getting things done. I am suspicious, however, of the conventional wisdom that senior management is synonymous with the management of change, except in so far as it reflects the truism that we live in an era of change. Management ought not to be about change for change's sake – sometimes indeed it ought to be about the preservation of continuity. More appealing, I think, is the notion that direction (in the sense used by Gordon Best and David Knowles in this book) is about the management of inherent tensions to achieve constructive results. That has several implications: that there must be a degree of confidence and trust between, for example, the health professions and the managers; that it is a management responsibility to ensure that the interests of patients and of the public are heard and given due weight. Most fundamental, perhaps, is the notion that the senior management function in health care is not simply about holding things in balance, and hence maintaining a position on the high wire, but about using tensions to achieve results.

I congratulate Fiona Hastings on making out of disparate elements a book that touches on important matters in a fresh and unpretentious way. Her final 'F', drawing on Rosabeth Moss Kanter, is 'F for fun', and health care management should be fun in the sense that the adrenalin level should be high. It is certainly not boring. The book manages – for me at least – to capture something of that sense of immediacy and relevance which is often totally missing from the management texts.

INTRODUCTION

FIONA HASTINGS

In 1990, the theme of 'Beyond Provider Dominance' commanded the presence of 29 top managers in Los Angeles. They came from five countries – Australia, Canada, Great Britain, the United States and New Zealand. Within the ranks were 13 clinicians, both doctors and nurses. This promised a lively debate – since those who represent professional providers may, at least prima facie, find what lies beyond their possible dominance either alarming or unattractive, as equally may those managing provider institutions!

The King's Fund was represented by its chief executive, Robert Maxwell, the then director of the King's Fund College, Gordon Best, and two College fellows. Our task was to try to manage the cultural, professional and national diversity in such a way that something greater than the sum of its parts might emerge.

Each delegate was required to provide a paper in advance to help anticipate and shape the debate. It is these which appear in a much edited form throughout this book.

As Robert Maxwell's paper demonstrates, the theme is topical, vital to the future of health care, and contentious. It is also wide ranging. Accordingly, the papers included philosophical questioning, political and economic analysis, large scale managerial and organisational issues and smaller scale discussions of specific instances. Some of these took the form of case studies with supporting documentation. Inevitably, individual perspectives were rooted in the value systems, organisational and managerial assumptions, the role of professionals and the overall nature of the health care delivery system in any one of five different nations. However, there were interesting parallels on the range of challenges faced by all.

THE SEARCH FOR AN ANSWER

Health policy and the structuring of health care delivery systems present a response to some kind of question, though this is often not expressly framed. The conference began with a quest – the hope that a gathering of experienced and dedicated individuals, being positively encouraged and

1

facilitated to think, talk and listen, might reach some general principles or ideas applicable in the real world and shed light on this issue.

However, as delegates wrestled to do this, it became clear that there were no 'right' answers to questions which in essence were about movement and change; definition of the location of any particular system or organisation was hard enough: predictions of the future or how to get there were inevitably vague, overly optimistic or pessimistic, too complex or over simple.

It was easier, initially, to agree important themes, questions and issues building on those noted in the Preface.

- Is there provider dominance? If so, is it good, bad, neutral, or inevitable, and how do we know which?
- If not, what does dominate?
- What other models or futures can be envisaged – are there lessons from the past?
- Who are providers?
- Professionals, managers, organisations and users are involved. What do we know about how they interact?
- Which of these appear to be gaining or losing in power or influence and why?
- What is the political, economic and social climate nationally and internationally?
- What is the role of power in any system and how does it move from one location to another?
- Who are the total numbers of 'players', and how do they leave or enter the 'game'?

In general, despite the absence of 'hard evidence', there was a consensus that provider dominance, loosely constructed, has been and is a 'problem' – and that in various ways it was changing. However, it can be guessed that a unified 'answer' to these and other broad questions did not appear. Instead, something interesting and more likely to be useful emerged.

It was clear that all five countries – in different ways – had to confront, simultaneously, issues involving financing, rationing, user power, the roles of professionals, health goals, the relation of health care to health, inequities including those affecting ethnic minorities, and upheavals in organisation structures. In addition, the 'reification' of provider dominance provided a link and a focus. The response of providers to the stimulus of change and their perceived power (whether real or imagined) to facilitate or block desired outcomes is often seen as crucial.

The attainment of goals or the solving of problems in key areas necessitated confronting providers – hospitals, professionals, the pharmaceutical, medical equipment and supply industries. The nature of the confrontation or exchange and the desired direction of movement was an issue for macro-policy makers from central governments right down to those responsible for particular services at the local level. Provider dominance elsewhere, in the food and tobacco industries most obviously, is clearly relevant to health if not to health care, and was also a continuing theme.

It appeared, intuitively at least, that improvements in health care and health are likely to emerge from effective and practical responses to specific problems in real life, rather than from theoretical arguments. The recognition that there was unlikely to be a new formula waiting in the wings was, in a way, liberating. Many ideas, masquerading as truths, had been tried and found wanting by most of us present. Accordingly, we turned our attention to the behaviour of important individuals and groups within existing systems as this can determine how issues are perceived. It can also structure possible actions or choices, and deliver outcomes which change things for better or for worse. This behaviour can be influenced in many ways. What follows in this book is an endeavour to pick up the material, both written and verbal, which was generated around and after this conference, and to link it to the field of managing organisational change in the complex world of health care. This change is concerned with moving beyond provider dominance but goes far in advance of this.

It is unlikely that any particular case or idea included here will be directly transferable to another location. What may be more easily absorbed as a general principle is that positive change has to be worked for with imagination, courage and humour, and that these qualities can be grown and developed.

I hope that the book will also be a small contribution, heavily dependant on the work of others, to a recognition that much of the organisation analysis common in the 1960s and 1970s, which led to inappropriate and unhelpful models, can now be safely jettisoned. What follows is not what purists may wish – well-organised theories firmly grounded in theories that went before. It is more like a work book. Those of us working in organisations can learn. We can learn from people like ourselves, who have tried and failed, or tried and succeeded, and occasionally have tried and not known whether to classify the outcome as failure or success! This is the real world inhabited by people like the delegates at this conference, and – I suspect – by anyone taking the trouble to read this book.

THE GEOLOGY OF ORGANISATION THEORY AND GURUS

FIONA HASTINGS

Once upon a time theory was seen in the abstract. A theory, once constructed, was independent of its creator. It could be understood without reference to its creator, and knowledge of the creator's individual views or personality was interesting only anecdotally. For some established principles, mainly in the pure sciences, these statements remain largely true. It is not necessary to understand Albert Einstein to understand $E=MC^2$.(*) The notion of theory as something separate from theoreticians falters a little when we move into human organisations. The whole field of sociology has been beset by this issue: it is often attacked for not being 'scientific', its writers may be accused of left-wing bias and (sometimes) of working to disrupt the very society which they claim to study.

The field of organisation analysis has hung somewhere between these two extremes. Thanks to F. W. Taylor's book, *The Principles of Scientific Management* (1), there has long been an assumption that designing and managing large organisations, originally within a capitalist free market system, could be studied 'scientifically'. That is to say:

● General observations allow the construction of a hypothesis.

● This hypothesis can then be tested using methods drawn from laboratories, or similar to them.

● If sufficient evidence is produced the theory can then be applied to other similar organisations. (**)

Hand in hand with this has marched psychology, or more particularly social psychology. Here again, a relationship with the biological aspect of humans has encouraged the belief in scientific psychology – in experiments, general principles and an individualistic focus. The two together have given us motivation, communication, and early leadership theories.

(*) It might be necessary, however, to understand the man to know why he was able to move beyond Euclidean geometry.
(**) Popperian not Kuhnian theory
(1) New York: Harper 1911

4

The assumptions behind the growth in this area of knowledge were, initially, largely unchallenged except by those who sought to dislodge capitalism or modern society in general. There were arguments of course, but, interestingly, the basic notion of organisation theory became generally acceptable, and was reflected in areas such as syllibi for courses at undergraduate level and within management programmes, including those in health. As a management teacher and trainer in the 1960s and 1970s, I found myself required by external examining bodies to take my students through a large body of knowledge, so that they could reproduce F. W. Taylor, A. Maslow, F. Hertzberg, L. Urwick and P. Drucker in much the same way that their engineering colleagues were absorbing the second law of thermodynamics. Even then, anecdotally, it was obvious to me that none of this made much difference to the actual behaviour of these individuals or to the organisations in which they worked. In fact, where it did have an effect, it often seemed perverse. Groups of employees resented the idea that their more senior managers could 'motivate' and 'structure' and 'communicate', as if their juniors were rather simple animals capable of only five levels of gratification, subject to two types of motivation and incapable of seeing through lies and deception.

The impetus for decline and greater questioning came largely from the United States. The roots lay in corporate failures, political decay and a recognition that these generally accepted theories had not been helpful in leading to successful organisations, with happy, well-motivated employees and a better overall society. In parallel, though of more questionable origins particularly in the late 1980s, came the headlong collapse of so called communist ideologies, where the application of macro-political and economic principles on a large scale had devastating consequences for individual communities and the world at large. The time had arrived to go back to basics and question all the assumptions about how to build successful organisations, whatever their purpose. Thankfully, this is increasingly being done, but not by seeking to replace Scientific Management parts 1 and 2 with parts 3 and 4. Instead, new and fresh approaches to ideas can be discerned.(*) One example, 'the art of story telling' was seen earlier to a degree in the case study form of teaching made famous at Harvard. However, there it was often regarded as evidence from which one could derive a new theory rather than evidence in its own right, directly transferable to the thoughts and actions of other managers or decision makers. Now it can be used more imaginatively to encourage creativity, lateral and upside down thinking. The crucial difference is the pre-eminence of real contemporary problem solving, as opposed to a search for relevant theories or a review of previously

(*) **New that is to say in the modern 'cultivated' west, but well known in so called primitive communities.**

addressed problems. Importantly, there is also encouragement for individuals that they can make a difference if they are prepared to challenge the present and dream the future.

MODERN GURUS

This change is reflected in the different way management writers are now seen. They are often 'personalities' in their own right, liable to be encountered in a whole variety of media and known for different things by different people. They can command large fees to contribute to management education programmes or to run consultancy activities for companies. They include Tom Peters and R. H. Waterman, Dick Beckhard, Henry Mintzberg, John Harvey-Jones, Charles Handy, Rosabeth Moss Kantor, James Hillman and even Douglas Adams of Hitchhiker fame. People reading their works will find things to agree with, things they find contentious and much with which they may profoundly disagree. The main difference, when compared to their 1960s and 1970s predecessors, is that they draw directly from evidence of a varied and rich nature and present ideas within loose frameworks for our judgement and consideration. They are eclectic, drawing from literature, history and biology, and are sometimes wilfully unscientific. It thus makes it easy for us to select and make use of aspects which may be applicable to our organisations and lives. We do not have to consider the world through the prism of established theories about hierarchies, span of control or levels of management. Readers can apply what they find to their own situations, can learn what they think by disagreeing with what they read or simply draw inspiration or encouragement for existing procedures. In addition, these contemporary gurus work as practising consultants to organisations and individuals, often using intuition, listening skills and consulting approaches to help their clients through change or transition.

In effect, this is empowerment of people working within organisations, and especially the management 'tribe'. This can be as important as empowering users or clients. In the right context, it can speed up the empowerment of others.

Thus inspiring key actors – or even irritating them – is likely to lead to greater improvements in organisations than trying to provide 'solutions' to unknown problems. Taking heart from these fresh ideas, I have structured the following chapters using a framework provided by one of the present day gurus. I could have chosen many but this one seems particularly apt.

Games

I have observed, while working in management development in the UK, how often games are used as analogies or metaphors; for example:
– the goal posts keep moving
– score an own goal
– pick up the ball and run with it
– score a bulls eye/home run/hit the target
– take your eye off the ball
– level playing-field
– team captain/coach
– reach the line
– shoot yourself in the foot.

'My' guru uses a game to illuminate her ideas – but a very different one played by strange people who either don't know 'our' rules or refuse to abide by them.

HOOPS AND HEDGEHOGS

This 'guru' is Rosabeth Moss Kantor. She is Professor of Business Administration at Harvard Business School and edits their influential journal. She has consulted widely and has written two important books, *The Change Masters* (2) and *When Giants Learn to Dance* (3). I have chosen to take a small part of her work which I find striking, and to shape the King's Fund conference papers and proceedings loosely around the framework which she presents.

Firstly, to the game, which feels to me closer to real life than more 'conventional' games where there are:
– two identified teams with similar strengths, skills and roles
– referees
– a time limit
– winners and losers and you know which is which
– a stadium or defined place
– a (largely) non-participating audience.

---

(2) **The Change Masters: Corporate entrepreneurs at work. London: Unwin, 1985.**
(3) **When Giants Learn to Dance. London: Simon & Schuster, 1989, Unwin paperback, 1990.**

Modern organisational 'games' have quite different characteristics:

- an unknown or unclear set of players, with an often changing and varying interest in the game

- no referees, several referees who may not agree, variable refereeing or players who are also referees

- unclear objectives – who is a winner – must there be a winner – are there other purposes?

- no single place to play

- home made equipment

- an audience which may join in.

If an organisation wants to 'win' in a game where the rules are unclear or may change arbitrarily, where various 'groups' involved may not conform – how then does it succeed? How does it ensure, also, that it doesn't lose? Rosabeth Moss Kantor has the very game. For grown up children who have forgotten their Lewis Carroll, I recommend you refresh your memory by glancing at *Alice in Wonderland* – (especially at the croquet game) (*). In this strange game the mallets become flamingoes whose necks continually move just as you want to hit the ball. The balls are hedgehogs who get up and move around. The hoops are playing cards which fall over in heaps and the event is supervised by the Queen of Hearts whose response to crisis is to shriek 'Off with their heads'. When all else fails, the Cheshire Cat appears to confuse the proceedings with a wicked smile.

So, if the target walks away, your senior management wants to execute you, and your tools don't or won't work, then you don't stand still and go on acting as if all was well, you respond – if you are wise! In order to respond you need to be, according to our guru:

(*) Another work, *The Hunting of the Snark*, also by Lewis Caroll, can be seen as analogous to much in health care – but that is another story.

Focused -   identification of what the manager or organisation is trying to do; clear specific goals, capable of translation into action, measurable, definable, understandable and implementable.

Fast -   empowered, creative, energetic players who 'own' the goals, want to win and don't allow their previous assumptions or 'map of the world' to act as a barrier to insight or action.

Flexible and friendly - wanting to work with the other players, senior managers and the tools – not against them or behind them. To which we could add Fun – the pursuit of serious matters need not be done seriously – fun fosters freedom.

This is Rosabeth Moss Kantor's 'F' plan. The five health care systems represented at the conference and the political, social and economic systems around them seem closer to this game of croquet than, for example, to archery. In archery, an individual known and practised skill is enough, while in croquet it probably is not, and the skill needed today may not be wanted tomorrow. Equally, team games like football, baseball or cricket do not really conform to typical organisational activity. (*)

The following papers have been arranged to highlight and match various attempts to improve health care delivery against these four 'F' characteristics. The cases and arguments are not uni-dimensional, and each paper has elements which may reflect all four either by their presence or absence!

Accordingly, I have not created a tight framework preferring to leave the reader to tease out relevant aspects (in the spirit of modern thinking!). However, the arguments do give us a theme for the 1990s, and some possible lessons which will be examined in the concluding section, in particular looking at dominant providers and the future.

Firstly, however, I have selected contributions which set the scene closer to health care and its dominant arenas – especially as we are trying to move beyond provider dominance.

(*) **Efforts, I suppose mainly by men, to make it so, may have contributed to unhelpful, combative ideas of how it all works.**

AN ORGANISATIONAL FRAMEWORK FOR CHANGE

Setting the scene

(Editor)

Much organisational analysis discusses the management of change and related issues. Interestingly, it is only relatively recently that the truly dynamic nature of this process has been revealed. In particular, the idea that 'management of change' is something that comes and goes and is more dominant at some times than at others has given way to a different perception. The received notion, common among many organisations and individuals, that change is somehow 'bad', will pass, and the idea that there was some 'golden age' where things were stable and predictable has, itself, been a force for change. The refusal of key organisations to see and interpret the forces around them has stored up huge problems both for themselves and others. This applies as much to the private sector – the failure of American business really to understand what the Japanese were capable of – as to the public sector, notably in the United Kingdom. Here, unreformed trade unions did not see the wall, let alone the writing. Professionals thought that 'we know best', and their evolved systems 'would last forever'. Many current writers are taking these ideas and moving them forward into areas of chaos theory (1) and predictions of how society may look in the relatively near future.

In the context of health care systems, this attitude to change has been critical, although it cannot necessarily be defined as anyone's fault. It may, indeed, be an inevitable consequence of a formal structural model of society, and of rational planning and its underlying assumptions.

In addition, where there are a large number of professional individuals (and groups) in powerful positions, each of them trained for and interested in working with individual patients, it becomes virtually impossible for any real corporate thinking to be done. Broader issues risk neglect, and then – partly for that reason – can overwhelm the organisation when they can be ignored no longer. The list is an impressive one – costs, outcomes, value for money, rationing, clinical audit, consumer choice, balance and location of

---

(1) Gluck, J. Chaos – making a new science. Viking Penguin 1987.

overall service provision, resource management, planning for health not health care – I could go on. Most of these were rarely addressed in any coherent way.

We thus saw an increasing dichotomy between experts and writers on social policy, the health care needs of populations, inequalities in health and the damage that health care could do (to health) and the people actually running health systems. The first contribution briefly addresses this issue, and provides a useful and simple backdrop as we consider cases and problems.

Professional and provider dominance in health care delivery has contributed to the apparent absence of good policy making, capable of being translated into effective action. Gordon Best and Len Schaeffer take this notion into the present and provide an interesting additional theme to the cases and histories which appear in this volume. In a complex, multi-professional organisation where hierarchies work only in part, such as in health care, the ability of senior managers to engage others in assessing the outside world is crucial. If they fail, many questions about effective political action, or organisational movement, have unpredictable outcomes.

MANAGING HEALTH CARE: THE 'GUIDANCE-DELIVERY' TENSION

GORDON BEST AND LEONARD SCHAEFFER
(UNITED KINGDOM)

GUIDANCE AND DELIVERY MANAGEMENT

In all large organisations it is possible to draw a distinction between two quite different but crucial types of management responsibility. At senior management levels, managers are typically concerned with organisation-wide issues related to the general health and survival of the organisation as a whole. At this level, managers in private sector organisations tend to have concerns such as the behaviour of competitors; changing market characteristics and consumer expectations; the public 'image' of the organisation; the welfare and motivation of employees; and, of course, 'bottom line' concerns such as profitability and efficiency. In large public sector organisations, senior managers will be dealing with some of the same issues as their private sector counterparts, but, in general, will be more interested in the external political environment than with the behaviour of competitors or the financial markets. Senior managers necessarily engage with these types of organisation-wide concerns because it is an important part of their job to establish organisational direction, to provide co-ordination and to motivate. In short, it is a crucial part of a senior manager's job to guide their organisation through the minefield of continually changing external circumstances so that, at a minimum, their organisation survives, and at best, it thrives and develops; hence the term 'guidance management'.

As one moves down through successive tiers of management, managers tend to become less concerned with organisation-wide guidance issues, and more concerned with managing the delivery of a product, service or other output that is crucial to – and is sometimes the *raison d'être* for – the organisation's survival. The distinction between guidance and delivery concerns is particularly clear in relation to the finance function. Thus, the director of finance in a large organisation will spend most of his/her time on organisation-wide guidance issues such as the behaviour of the finance and money markets, the forward prices of commodities central to the organisation's production processes, and profit per employee ratios for different lines. But again, as one moves through levels of management, those operating within the finance function become increasingly concerned with the delivery of financial services: for example, seeing to it that bills are paid; that salaries and wages are paid; and that senior management receive timely, accurate and relevant information about the financial performance of the organisation as a whole.

All organisations operate in continually changing, difficult-to-predict environments. The challenges, problems and opportunities facing guidance managers continually mutate – often at very short notice. As a result, there is continual and shifting tension between the demands placed on guidance management, and the requirements for effective delivery management. For example, guidance managers like to be able to re-define 'the rules of the game' so that they have the flexibility to respond to new opportunities (or parry new threats) at short notice. Delivery managers, by contrast, prefer a reasonably stable environment so that they can guarantee the quality and reliability of their services or products. The tension is perhaps more vividly illustrated in the situation where the director of marketing wishes to secure a new customer by promising the immediate delivery of a product (guidance concern), but where the production engineer is worried that this will push throughput to the point where product quality will be threatened (delivery concern).

As with all distinctions in management, this one is not cut and dried. For example, during crises, guidance managers often take delivery decisions that override the wishes of delivery managers. Equally, when major guidance decisions are pending (for example, entering a new market), key delivery managers are often invited into the 'Board Room' to contribute to the decision. Nevertheless, the distinction can be a useful one, and there is a growing body of evidence, mostly from verbal reports, which suggests that successful large organisations are often those which manage well the tension between guidance and delivery. (*)

THE GUIDANCE–DELIVERY TENSION IN HUMAN SERVICE ORGANISATIONS

In large organisations which provide or arrange for the provision of human services (for example, education, health and certain types of leisure services), the tension between guidance and delivery management is particularly important. Moreover, the successful management of this

---

(*) **Busy managers rarely write!**

tension is, arguably, central to the quality of the service experienced by the client/customer. There are a number of reasons for this, but the following are among the most important:

- The clients of human service organisations tend to become a part of the organisation while they are receiving/purchasing the service. During this time, they are often 'under the control' of delivery managers.

- Those who manage the delivery of human services are often professionals or 'experts' who require a certain amount of delivery 'autonomy' if they are to provide a high quality service (for example, doctors, teachers or airline pilots).

- In the delivery of human services, there is often a conflict between providing clients with what they want, as distinct from what they need. This complicates the problem of deciding what constitutes a high quality service and, therefore, what constitutes a reliable 'bottom line'.

- The performance of guidance and delivery managers in human service organisations is judged against very difficult criteria and on very different time scales. Thus, it may take months or years for a major guidance decision to have a detectable impact on the quality of service delivery. This further complicates the problem of identifying a reliable 'bottom line'.

Despite these and other difficulties, some human service organisations do tend to manage the guidance-delivery tensions more successfully than other. Most airlines, for example, time when to raise guidance concerns. For example, they would not raise with pilots in mid-flight, the need to conserve airline fuel in the light of recent price increases, but would wait until the pilots have landed and are no longer engaged in the management of delivery. Health care organisations the world over, however, have still to discover how to persuade or oblige their principal deliverers (that is, doctors and other clinicians) to take guidance concerns seriously. Examining how senior health care managers in the different participating countries are attempting to manage this and other key guidance-delivery tensions within their organisations is a major organisation issue at present. The success – or otherwise – of it, will have an influence on the role of providers in the future, and their relationship with payers.

Empowering to action
(Editor)

As this book progresses, the theme of enabling key actors in organisations, particularly senior managers, to implement any policy at all emerges as crucial. Arguably, many well-intentioned reorganisations or reforms fail when this is not accomplished.

This phenomenon was discerned by A. Wildavsky (1), as long ago as 1979. He researched and identified 'the implementation gap' in the field of public policy. Put simply, ideas or policies (guidance), however good and appropriate, can completely fail to impact. The complexities of modern society, and the unpredictability of key actors within their organisations, make it virtually impossible to be certain of the consequences of planned change. Another way of describing it is that levers are pulled by politicians or civil servants, but they are either not connected to anything at all or are connected up in a way not understood. Sometimes this results in minimal outcomes, sometimes perverse or paradoxical outcomes, and sometimes all that happens is the problem moves from one place and settles down in another.

A good current example in the United Kingdom concerns the massive increase in homelessness and vagrancy caused by closing down large institutions for people with mental health problems, without enough alternative support – surely not what was intended?

David Knowles, until recently a senior manager within the British National Health Service, has contributed some thoughts which complement Gordon Best and Len Schaeffer's paper. His paper discusses a particular management issue which he faced, putting it in the context of:

- current and continuing changes in the National Health Service;
- guidance-delivery tension; and
- the implementation gap.

He doesn't come to any particularly tidy conclusions, but, interestingly, notes that one of the key considerations has to be about creating good managers who can do several impossible things before breakfast and balance many conflicting interests and themes. Organisation and management development are not luxuries, but necessities for effective action.

(1) **Wildavsky, A. Speaking Truth and Power: The art and craft of policy analysis. Boston 1979.**

GUIDANCE–DELIVERY TENSION: AN APPROACH TO MANAGEMENT AND ORGANISATION DEVELOPMENT

DAVID KNOWLES (UNITED KINGDOM)

INTRODUCTION

The National Health Service has embarked on a major reorganisation of its health care delivery system, and the Government is seeking to implement change on a comprehensive basis within a short timescale.

There is a general perception from payer (Government), from providers and from patients (the community) that the reforms challenge the existing values and culture of the NHS. The existing delivery system is characterised by an ethos of caring and community service, sustained by a relatively bureaucratic and highly structured organisation. The reforms substitute a delivery system which, while still focusing on the ethos of caring and community service, derives its strength from competition and differentiation of functions. The objective is to generate added value by higher productivity and improved quality.

This paper considers whether this aspiration is realistic. It will focus on the changes in the balance of power between providers and patients, in the context of how the process of making the inevitable choices on the margins of health care might evolve. An objective will be to establish connections between the short term agenda, dominated by meeting Government targets for the implementation of structural and organisational changes, and a longer term view which ensures management capability to maintain positive and evolutionary development of the health care delivery care model. This reinforces a view of a role of senior health executives as a focus for guiding the organisation in coping with externally imposed change and responding to the changing environment within which health care services are provided, while sustaining the more traditional roles of leadership and effective delivery of services.

The analysis derives from two of the key themes of the seminar – the balancing of the differing values of providers and purchasers, and the process of managing the new tensions between them.

16

MAKING CHOICES:
THE PURCHASER/PROVIDER/PATIENT
TENSIONS

One of the most significant elements of guidance-delivery/tension derives from the situation in which, for all practical purposes, there is in all health care systems relatively infinite demand and need, but finite resources. This makes inevitable the exercise of choice, whether implicit or explicit, in the determination of services to be provided. These choices usually apply only on the margins of a health care delivery system, but over time they determine the shape and configuration of services that are provided for the community.

The fundamental dilemma for Government, in its role as payer in the UK system, is that, while the 'bottomless pit' syndrome is readily acknowledged in private, the public posture is compromised by the reality of politics. The political party in power might wish to open up a dialogue with the people they represent and serve about the inevitability of making choices, and therefore of choosing not to provide some services either at the volume or quality level which is perceived by the people to be needed. To do so can be to present easy political advantage to the party in opposition.

Thus, the recent NHS reforms were presented in terms of added value by increased productivity and improved quality, with the certainty that even if these benefits are realised, there will still be the problems which derive from the inability to meet all perceived needs or demands for health care. The recognition that that would apply even if Government increased the real resources available to the NHS, only serves to heighten a sense of futility. This reinforces, first, a degree of political cynicism, and second, a pragmatic determination to deal with the problems of the NHS by essentially short term, palliative measures.

For the providers of health care, the tensions focus on the irreconcilable demands of the individual patient with those of the community as a whole. The providers of health care – doctors, nurses and other professional carers – have the security blanket of their professionalism and an ethical code which requires optimum care and treatment for the individual patient or client that presents. The macro problem of the balancing of the level and quality of service between groups of patients or clients can easily be suppressed. Indeed, it would be unreasonable to expect the professionals delivering health care to individual patients to re-focus their values and professional ethos. They should, however, be made aware of the context and process for the making of the choices which determine the shape and configuration of

17

health services, if only to avoid their easy retreat to the high moral ground when confronted with the consequences of choice. Of course, ideally the objective should be aimed higher; to generate some informed participation from professionals in an objective and explicit process which informs choices.

For the community and for the patients, the tensions derive from the frustrations of experiencing or observing unmet needs and low quality of provision. While this only occasionally takes the form of criticism and challenge to professional and technical standards, there is a widespread and well documented dissatisfaction with other aspects of service. This often derives from low quality services delivered sometimes in an uncaring and neglectful manner, which can, with marginal improvements of supervision, management and morale, be improved. Many of these concerns, however, reflect an NHS where the support services have been squeezed well beyond reasonable margins of cost effectiveness as a result of extreme financial pressures.

At the centre of these tensions felt by payers, providers and patients, and deriving substantially from the reality of the infinite demand/finite resources dilemma, are the managers. They, in practice, are in the business of building bridges, of diffusing tension and of seeking to establish a reasonable balance of services – direct and indirect – to be delivered within the inevitable constraints of available resources.

THE PROCESS OF DETERMINING PRIORITIES

The theory of how managers should determine these priorities in the NHS is relatively straightforward, though the practice a good deal less so.

There is a base line of policy frameworks to inform necessary choices, which usually comprise a national, a regional and a local view of relative priorities. This, however, is a rational model. The reality is also significantly influenced by other considerations which have the effect of distorting priorities. Two such influences are particularly significant.

First, there is the impact of a political process which struggles to come to terms with the constraint of finite resources and does not want to exchange one service element for another, even when the added value on some objective scale does evidence clear advantage in the exchange. This is a tough proposition even when the choice is within the same hospital or district. Translate that choice into a geographical equation of value between services in different districts or regions and the consequence can be a political minefield. The proffered ideal is that there should be continual growth of available resources to ensure that the choice process relates always to the most effective deployment of the new resources for service developments. Quite apart from the inevitability in the UK of differential allocation of development resources, there is little evidence that governments in recent years have either the will or the capacity to sustain growth at a level which can reasonably fuel this aspiration.

The second distorting influence derives from the activities of the providers and, particularly, the single most powerful group of providers in the UK system – the consultants. They constitute the most significant provider influence lobby in the political process which determines the reality of change at the local district and hospital level, and they tend to be heavily predisposed in favour of specialised acute hospital based services. Their impact on the decisions being made which change the shape and configuration of services is often, as a consequence of that instinctive preference, in conflict with the strategic direction that derives from the national policy frameworks.

Managers are left with a major problem in determining how, legitimately and practically, to respond to the pressures to change the shape of services provided.

CASE STUDY:
THE RIVERSIDE EXPERIENCE –
EMPOWERING THE COMMUNITY

Riverside is a large Central London health authority which manages ten hospitals, including two major teaching hospitals and community-based services for its resident population of 280,000. Its current revenue allocation is £170m and it employs 8,500 staff.

Ten years ago it was evident that there was a need for rationalisation of its hospital facilities, which would involve substantial reduction of capacity and the closure of some hospitals. By virtue of their Central London location and consequential 'establishment' connections, most of the hospitals in the district had high media profiles, which would have the effect of making closure difficult to implement and politically controversial. Yet there was a need to respond, both to the external environment which was imposing reductions in the revenue baseline of the district, and to the internal pressure to improve the quality of services in hospitals, some, or at least large parts, of which were well past their 'sell by date'. There was also the pressure to develop 'priority' services which, in many instances, were grossly inadequate within the district (at that time, for example, there was no local investment in services for people with learning difficulties).

What was evident, however, in the early 1980s was the lack of any coherent framework within which change could be effectively managed, nor was there any sense of legitimacy in the process of changing the shape and configuration of health services in the district to respond to the external and internal pressures. There was, of course, no shortage of aspiration and ambition for service development, but this was isolated from any understanding of how this could be achieved in an environment of declining revenue resources.

An early notion in the district was some attempt 'to empower the community'. It derived from an acknowledgement of the inevitability of making choices on the margins of health care in Riverside which would create both advantage and disadvantage for the community – by which term there was a sense of both the community for whom services were provided, and the community of providers of services.

In retrospect, it is possible to identify three distinct phases to what was identified at the beginning, albeit a little pompously, as the strategy for empowering the community.

i) Sharing the context

The first phase was to establish a wider understanding of the context in which policies relating to the volume and quality of services provided in the district were determined. In a project which was undertaken with the assistance of Tom Evans, then director of the King's Fund College, a review was undertaken of the condition of services provided and this was then set against an analysis of the demands for, influences on and constraints around possible service changes.

A framework was generated which specified mission, overall objectives and guiding principles, which then became the basis for criteria which could be used to evaluate policy options for change. Two reports entitled *Evaluation of Health Services: A strategic framework for the future Volumes I and II* were produced in 1983 and 1984 and used as a basis for what was intended to be an exercise in public consultation which focused not on specific proposals, but rather a policy context within which future health care policy would be determined. The objectives were to generate a wider validation of the analysis, inform a shared understanding of the constraints on policy options and engender a sense of legitimacy in moving forward on a difficult agenda on behalf of the community.

Much interest was generated, with many and varied meetings attended by staff, representatives of local government, MPs, voluntary organisations and members of the general public. In a situation in which these people were well accustomed to exercises of formal consultation, the absence of a specific proposal was both an advantage (debate was usually open and dialogue constructive) and a disadvantage (a cynicism about the motivation; the fear of 'nasties' in the pipeline; and, for some, the irritation of a process for which a yes/no answer was not required).

While we found that 'empowering' was too ambitious a concept, many people acquired better understanding of and interest in the macro issues of health care, and were stimulated to seek a more consistent and regular involvement in health care planning in the district.

ii) Multi-scenario planning

The second phase evolved in the mid-1980s. By then, significant downsizing and service rationalisation in the district had become inevitable and, perhaps equally significantly, that inevitability had been generally acknowledged, particularly among consultant medical staff. However, while the 'sharing the context' exercise had facilitated a broader-based analysis of the macro policies which combined to require potentially radical changes in health care services in the district, there was no capacity to determine how to respond, other than by a series of limited short term palliative measures, which offered no vision for the future. For many, this constituted a failure of imagination and a policy of 'death by a thousand cuts'. 'Sharing the context' had led to an understanding of the need for a coherent response to the problems, but had provided no framework for determining that response.

With help from Gordon Best, who had succeeded Tom Evans as director of the King's Fund College, and Greg Parston, also of the College, a group of senior managers and clinicians began to explore the experience of commercial organisations and health services in other countries (notably Ottawa in Canada) with multi-scenario planning. The mid-1980s was the time of the culmination of a long process in the NHS of rational planning. All levels in the

NHS produced strategic plans, usually from inadequate and inaccurate data bases, and all characterised by a straight line projection of life as it was to become in some distant year in the calendar. Those who had been first into this world of long term strategic planning were beginning to realise that their predictions of the future had not, for perfectly good reasons, proved to be accurate. On the whole, this tended to produce a rationalisation along the lines of determining to do it better next time, rather than any fundamental re-appraisal of the process.

Multi-scenario planning was an alternative response which established a context and framework within which managers might make the managerial decisions required of them, without, as far as possible, compromising a range of predicted future scenarios. It was a process that acknowledged the inevitability of uncertainty and sought to create an organisational culture which coped with it and retained a capacity to make essential decisions impinging on the future shape and configuration of services.

The range of medium to long term scenarios, described in terms of the influences of demand (population, epidemiology, medical practice and technology) and supply (health and social policy, resources, medical practice and technology) became supplementary criteria for the evaluation of policy options.

A report, the *Riverside Strategic Framework*, was published in 1986. It sought consultation on a range of future scenarios, the consequential evaluative criteria and an initial list of possible options for the re-configuration of hospital services.

The consultation exercise was mainly characterised by relief that at last some solid, if unpopular, options were out in the open and that therefore there was something to protest, to demonstrate, to petition against. Nevertheless, for some, there was an appreciation of the attempt to establish a framework within which choices could be made. That this framework had a logic stemming from the multi-scenario planning process, and a legitimacy derived from the successive attempts to 'empower' the community, (patients and providers) was also recognised as establishing a base from which radical changes to the shape of health care services could be reasonably implemented.

iii) The Westminster and Chelsea Hospital Project

In 1988, the District published for consultation its proposals to rationalise hospital services. The plan, in summary, was to close five hospitals (total beds 1200, and including one of London's famous teaching hospitals, the Westminster, which provides services for a small but distinctive area of Central London), build a new 650-bed teaching hospital, plus five nursing homes for elderly people and elderly people with a mental illness, and a primary health care centre. The project was planned to be completed on an unprecedented – for the NHS – timescale of three and a half years with capital costs to be covered by the sale of the land released following closure of the hospitals, and with an annual revenue saving of £18m.

The project was approved by the Secretary of State in the House of Commons on 22 December 1988 following a long, controversial and exciting year of consultation! It is now to a large extent implemented, but regretfully, falling land prices in London had a negative effect.

Reflecting on the process over a period of nearly ten years, there is evidence that it reduced to some degree the tensions which pervade the task of making choices on the margins of health care. Some people, however, have concluded that it was little more than a complex and protracted 'softening up' process to facilitate and make more palatable politically imposed cuts in service. Others have seen it as a smokescreen to obscure what proved to be the reality of service reductions.

My own conclusion is that the original notions of 'empowering the community' and 'legitimatising the decision making processes' can now be seen to fall within a spectrum from well meaning naivety to presumptuous arrogance. Nevertheless, there is a thread running through the process which has facilitated change. Increasingly, the very radical re-structuring of hospital and community services is regarded as a major opportunity for delivering improved value in health services and consistent with a shared, negotiated and coherent vision for the future. It has been the means of, at least, opening up to general scrutiny the sources of tensions in the system, not merely for managers, but also for politicians, for providers of health care services (especially consultants) and for some of the representatives of, and proxies for, the community of people who use our services.

IMPLICATIONS FOR ORGANISATIONAL DEVELOPMENT

The tensions of payers, providers and patients which focus on the problems of making the choices which determine the overall shape and configuration of services – the choices on the margins – will not diminish as a result of the NHS reforms. The fundamental problem of determining what services should not be provided, or what quality standards cannot be achieved, will still confront those who emerge from the re-structuring with the central responsibility of ensuring that the volume of service provided matches the level of available resources.

However, there is optimism that the effect of the reforms will focus more clearly on and make more explicit the rationing processes. A key principle of the reforms is the separation of the responsibility for the purchasing and commissioning of health services from that of the provision of health care services. Initially, that separation will be achieved mainly by changes in the internal organisation of local (district) health authorities. From April 1991 a minority of the provider units were separated from the health authorities and have become self-governing NHS Trusts. Since April 1992 many more have joined and a majority of the remainder of providers have applied or expressed interest.

Meanwhile, the main activity of the local health authorities will be on the purchasing role, in which they will commission, within available resources, health care systems for the local community.

To achieve this there are three elements of organisational development which will be focused in districts. First, establishing viable and effective, but separate, organisational entities for provision of services (Trusts and DMUs) and a purchasing unit. Second, determining the linkages between these separate units. Third, identifying the framework for the 'arms length relationship' between the health authority, its chief executive officer (district general manager) and its chief finance officer, and the separate organisational units for which it is ultimately accountable. In effect, these will comprise the rules of intervention.

The context, which informs the process for determining priorities and choices, was described earlier as a mixture of rational (the national, regional and local policy frameworks) and the practical impact of consumer, political and, most significantly, provider pressures. Experience in the UK often seems to confirm that the latter is at least as significant as the former. The clear separation of purchasing and providing responsibilities offers the opportunity to re-assert the legitimacy of the former, especially if it can be demonstrated to be derived, in a greater measure than has previously been achieved, from and on behalf of the community.

Certainly, if local health authorities do develop a clear sense of responsibility for maximising the effectiveness of the services they purchase for their local communities, and keep that separate from their residual and diminishing responsibility for the provision of health care through DMUs, then the extent of provider-driven distortions of the desired pattern of health care service is reduced. However, the reality of empowering the community will necessarily require the identification of proxies for that community – groups or individuals who can reasonably be expected to share the context within which local health authorities will be making the marginal choices.

Elected representatives of the community (members of parliament, councillors in the associated local authorities) will claim, with better justification than anyone else, legitimacy in that role. Their willingness to be associated with the exercise of choice which reflects the infinite demand/finite resource dilemma has not often been demonstrated in the past and there is nothing in the reforms which justifies any expectation that that situation will change. Health authorities will, no doubt, seek to broaden the base of their consultative processes to generate better definition of the community's needs and also to improve understanding of the policy context for the decisions relating to the application of available resources. This will involve a range of voluntary and statutory organisations locally, including the community health councils, who ought to see the influencing of purchasing decisions as a practical extension of their role as the advocate of the individual consumers of health care.

There is also an expectation that the general medical practitioners (GPs) will assume much greater significance in the exercise of influence on policy choices by the local health authority.

IMPLICATIONS FOR MANAGEMENT DEVELOPMENT

This analysis points to the inevitability of managerial responsibility for the effective determination of those policies which address issues of choices and priorities on the margins of health care resources. While these decisions will usually be taken in the name of health authorities and will reflect national, regional and local policy frameworks, it will be the managers, particularly those in the purchasing arms of the organisation, who will discharge these responsibilities. These decisions will continue to reflect a negotiating process in which an attempt is made to generate a balance between the expectations and demands of payers, providers and patients.

In suggesting that this key task will fall particularly to those who have the responsibility for purchasing services for their local community, it is not intended to under-estimate the task of managing the provider units. The perceptions, particularly of patients and the community generally, of the quality and effectiveness of services will mainly reflect the managerial focus and commitment in those provider units. However, that presents a management development process with which there is great familiarity in the UK and in other countries.

What presents as distinctive in management development terms from the UK reforms is the impact on those managers who will be developing the purchasing function, with its central focus on maximising value for the community from available resources, and therefore having an explicit process and coherent framework for determining choices on the margins of health care provision. Some of the issues that can already be seen as needing to be focused in the management development process, for this newly conceived purchasing function, include:

- understanding how leverage can be generated and responsibility exercised

- what size of organisation is appropriate to balance sensitivity to consumer and community needs with the capacity to negotiate cost-effective service contracts

- determining the range of skills and 'management competencies' that will be needed to make the purchasing function effective.

More significant, however, will be the need for managers to give leadership in establishing a coherent process for determining choices between levels of services to be provided and the quality standards to be generated. This will be important in the achievement of the initial phase of implementation of the Government's NHS reforms. Equally significantly it will need to be complemented by the development of a longer term vision of how health services might evolve both locally and nationally. This will require flexibility and strategies which can cope with political, as well as financial, changing circumstances. Learning to adapt and respond to this condition of uncertainty is a requirement on managers if some consistency of policy direction is to be sustained.

Generating this kind of managerial culture also provides the most effective means for managers to respond to the tensions which derive from the different expectations of Government, providers and community and which focus on an unwillingness to acknowledge, or a lack of understanding of, the inevitability of making choices on the margins of health care.

What Sir Bryan Thwaites (1) describes as the developing dilemma deriving from 'increasingly unsatisfiable expectations' creates an environment in which there will be increasing tensions between Government, providers and community focused on the rationing and priority setting processes. It will be the most senior executives within the NHS who will have to manage these tensions and assume responsibility both for delivering effective services and determining priorities and making choices on the margins of health care.

The prospect is for a rationing and decision making process which is more community oriented and which can generate added service value in terms of volume and quality, but this will require changes in the management culture in the NHS and better focused organisational and management development.

Concluding thoughts
(Editor)

Understanding how to 'get things done', and establishing new ways of thinking about such issues, is as important as creating direction and vision. Within the context of organisations managing change (that is all of them), we have, so far, identified some simple but vital questions.

1) *Does it have a mechanism, a place, a set of behaviours and any skill to understand guidance?*

2) *Has it understood that traditional linear planning models are not only unhelpful but dangerous?*

3) *Has it learned how to manage flexible scenarios and involve those affected by them?*

4) *Has it considered how and by whom any plans are going to be translated into action?*

5) *Has it included management and organisation development as part of the entire process?*

6) *Has it learned the 'F' lessons (see Chapter I) to which the book now returns?*

---

(1) Thwaites, Sir Bryan. The NHS: The end of the rainbow?. University of Southampton 1987.

THE 'F' PLAN PART I: GET FOCUSED

Robert Maxwell notes in his introduction the need for some idea of direction to allow meaningful choices to be made. Equally, David Knowles revisits the territory where too much clarity about direction makes us blind and insensitive towards what is actually happening or fresh opportunities which may present. Consequently, the idea of focus as the operational word rather than direction or goal or objective is a particularly useful one. It implies realism, and the adaptation of the onlooker to what they are looking at and something which must, therefore, be continually changing – as caught by a camera. Keen photographers could take the metaphor further. A camera shows what it shows and no more; focus and other tricks can be used to make pictures harsher or softer, further or nearer or to change colour. So, in order to focus, we have to be clear what it is we wish to look at, who is going to look with us and to have some appropriate mechanism for that interaction. This could be criticised as a rather woolly and vague notion, yet it seems to be more helpful and much closer to the reality of the world we inhabit, which in the field of health care is crucial.

Increasingly, it appears that we have not really looked at anything much in particular, and when we do, we frequently select the wrong targets. We have also been unclear as to who is doing the looking or who also should look, and we have lacked mechanisms for that process. It does seem to me that the humble word 'focus', imaginatively interpreted, provides its own crispness and encourages managers really to clarify for themselves and others what is in view.

Related words are much discussed: 'vision' and 'mission' have become commonplace notions, though often, it has to be said, with a grimace or a wry, if discreet, chuckle from the listeners. We seem to find it very hard to move from the familiar – the idea of a goal and a relationship with the old games already discussed.

The papers which I have selected for this chapter illuminate these ideas in different ways. There is no simple series of steps from establishing the focus to moving into appropriate action. The basic idea of focus as noted is that it permits a look. All the rest of the work remains to be done. This work may require fundamental changes in people's previous perceptions, real and quite painful consideration of differing value choices and acknowledgement of psychological behaviour such as denial and blame. The papers, thus, do not offer any solutions. They simply take further the struggle which managers must engage in once they have decided really to look.

28

1988, 1990 AND BEYOND

An earlier King's Fund conference in 1988 had as its theme 'Managing For Health Result'.(1) This represented a drive towards 'focus' – a movement away from responding to individual patients on a largely ad hoc basis by consultants towards an ideal of 'results'. The debate continues about 'health gain' and its role in any health care system mainly concerned with repairs. Health gain, in fact, seems to be more concerned with the wider environment – transport, pollution, education, housing, employment and genetics. Nevertheless, it has provided a new focus, changed the nature of the process of decision taking at various levels and the arena in which health is discussed.

Our theme, 'Beyond Provider Dominance' (and the hidden assumption that it represents a 'block'), requires us to assess deficiencies in the present system, and how, therefore, a future one might be better. This, in turn, may contribute to improved health result, gain or care. The first paper in this section, by Steve Leeder, restates the initial problem whereby provider dominance has little to do with health outcomes – and reminds us that such dominance in other markets (for example, the food or tobacco industry) is probably even more associated with health, or its absence. It is a useful bridge between our two most recent ventures.

---

(1) Later published as a report. Carle, Nan (ed). Managing for Health Result. King Edward's Hospital Fund for London 1990.

REORIENTATING THE HEALTH CARE SYSTEM TOWARDS HEALTH RATHER THAN MEDICINE

STEVEN R LEEDER (AUSTRALIA)

Australia, Canada, the US and parts of Europe have recently begun to devote tiny fragments of their care resources to the exploration of ways in which health and prevention goals can be set. In Australia, these new goals are located in a health care system which has much system, of considerable administrative and fiscal sophistication, but with little to do with health. Its ethos can be crudely summed up as 'counting eggs but not knowing what's hatching'. The level of cost-accounting in the health system is so precise that it is possible to learn the catering bill for a large hospital down to the last egg. At the same time, there are virtually no formal outcome measures of health status improvements attributed to the interventions whose cost elements we know in microscopic detail.

That administrative interest in outcomes is so underdeveloped is not accidental – there are no rewards or sanctions within the system for outcomes, but there are hundreds for budgetary control. The concerns thus remain very largely with making sure the budget is not over-spent.

It is true that practising clinicians take some, or indeed many, of their decisions on the basis of what they believe or know they are achieving, but, unlike the administrators who know lots about the costs involved, they traditionally have only hazy ideas of what these outcomes actually cost to achieve. Thus, administrators know a massive amount about system (as distinct from programme) costs and clinicians know nothing much about costs but hold all the knowledge there is at present about outcomes. It is akin to having logistics and artillery units that have no idea of each other's imperatives or targets.

It is pointless to say that the available output (*) measures are informative; for even though they may be so in some abstract, managerial sense, they have little or nothing to do with health improvement, and only minuscule relevance to the concerns of the consumer. Even when

---

(*) **A distorting euphemism in this context, tempting us, for example, to value a surgical operation more highly than preventing the need for one.**

30

considering such output measures, we have no formal data source relevant to staff satisfaction, patient satisfaction (other than letters of commendation or complaint), employment or overall impact on the economy.

There is a determined conspiracy of ignorance about the relationship of investment to health outcome, favoured by many doctors who ascend the high moral ground by insisting that every life is infinitely valuable and that everything they do is in the patient's best interest – as if that were a failsafe guide to policy making which would clear up all this nonsense about resources if only the administrators would adopt it. This may have been tolerable in the faraway time when little that was effective could be done with health care resources, but not now when a great deal more things which are apparently effective can be done than we can pay for.

Do we need more money for health care – or is it really for medical well-being? The irony is that, under these arrangements, the medical profession retains an almost monopolistic control over the expenditure of the so called health care dollar (which administrators are then asked to administer), while much of the common, intractable and uninteresting health problems in the community are judged out of the range of high-tech medical care. Under these circumstances of provider dominance, we are investing more but paying less attention to the frequent, troubling health problems of our time.

As Navarro states in his critique of the world's health problems at the time of WHO Alma Ata agreement (1), the unconscious collusion among middle class professionals world-wide, including (and perhaps especially) doctors, is one of the major inhibitors of achieving anything even vaguely resembling equity in health opportunity in most of the world today. Middle class medicine is hi-tech medicine, and it seems that the environment doesn't matter: 'we should be free to practice this style of medicine in Madagascar or Manhattan'.

Lest this be thought of as a uniquely third world phenomenon, let me recount an example from Australia: mammography in the Northern Territory.

As part of a federal election campaign, the then Australian prime minister, Mr Bob Hawke, told Australian women that his future government would introduce a government-funded programme of mammographic screening – despite the fact that government-funded pilot evaluations had not yet been completed. This was in response to a most improbable provider-consumer coalition comprising the women's health lobby and diagnostic radiologists, aided and abetted by some

---

(1) Navarro, V. 'A critique of the ideological and political position of the Brandt Report and the Alma Ata declaration.' International Journal of Health Services 1984, v14(2) 159-172.

epidemiologists who believe that the evidence is quite firm that mammography, despite its immense costs, has a worthwhile benefit. As part of this programme a mobile mammography unit was offered to the Northern Territory government by the commonwealth. It was worth about $400,000. It was a symbol of unadulterated provider dominance.

The Northern Territory covers one sixth of the total land mass of Australia, and has about 4000 women of 50 years or older living in widely disparate places (islands, small townships, and so on) joined by a poorly developed network of roads. How a mobile service was meant to serve their needs is unclear, but a senior Northern Territory political figure said to a senior health official, 'Well, I understand your medical concerns, but if I don't accept this bloody thing from the Commonwealth I'll be hammered by the women's lobby.' The service, with the vicissitudes of distance, quality control and uptake, will cost about $600,000 a year to run. Meanwhile Aboriginal consumers (or their children) continue to die of diarrhea.

A dominant characteristic of the world-wide medical care system, so devastatingly criticised by Halfdan Mahler in his crusade to achieve reasonable levels of health for all, is that it operates for the emotional and intellectual comfort of sickness care providers and, to a lesser extent, administrators.(*) It has no explicit goals that relate to health. The goals that exist are densely fiscal (administrators, please stand up) or pseudo-moral or selfishly materialistic (providers, your turn now) and have nothing explicit to do with making people well in a measurable, objective sense.

ENTER THE BETTER HEALTH COMMISSION

Australia is probably no better and no worse than most other countries in this regard. In this confusing and unsatisfactory context, in 1985, the Better Health Commission (BHC) was established by the Australian Federal Minister for Health, Dr Neal Blewett.

By disposition and experience, Blewett was primed to address the larger structural issues about health care that include questions about goals, equity and efficiency of the health care system.

The BHC's brief was to compose a set of goals and targets for Australia which reflected its commitment to the World Health Organisation's Alma

---

(*) In his closing remarks to the 43rd World Health assembly in Geneva in 1988, just before his retirement, Mahler referred to the groups which had 'totally failed' to convince to put their weight behind Health for All – the medical practitioners and the universities!

Ata agreement to foster primary health care with a view to providing reasonable levels of health for all the world's people by the year 2000. Because it had a membership that included several non-health professionals, and because its purpose seemed 'soft', it was regarded with derision by many traditional health care providers, especially the medical profession.

The BHC was asked to consult widely in the community to determine the ways in which interest groups, professionals and consumers would like to see health care delivered in the future, and to set goals and targets for the improvement of Australia's health and, especially, to seek ways of alleviating the inequalities of access to health and (probably) health care experienced by groups of varied economic advantage.

Consultation and public hearings around Australia revealed a powerful coalition of non-medical interests in prevention which, at the time, as now, consumed less than 0.008 per cent of Australia's GDP (that is 1 per cent of the 7.8 per cent of GDP Australia devotes to health care altogether). A submission was received from only one Dean of Australia's ten medical schools; a powerful indicator of its non-acceptance by traditional medical interests.

The BHC's report, *Looking Forward to Better Health* (2), set an agenda which contained 19 major recommendations ranging from a review of public health education and professional development through to the establishment of an Australia-wide, consensually-accepted National Programme for Better Health.

Following on from the Better Health Commission, an effort was made to involve the States and consumers more fully.

After the tabling of the BHC report by Blewett, Minister of Health, in the Federal Parliament, little happened for months. Although the proposals had notional price tickets attached to them, they still elicited no bureaucratic or administrative response. Discussions I had with Blewett at that time revealed his feeling that we had not invested sufficient time and energy in 'selling' the proposals to the States and Territories. This required some strategic rethinking of the issue.

Stephen Leeder continued his paper with some of the specific political and administrative steps which moved Australia closer towards implementing a national programme for better health. As in most countries, this proved difficult and frustrating.

---

(2) *Looking Forward to Better Health* **was a three-volume report which contained: in Volume 1, the major recommendations and findings of the Commission; in Volume 2, the reports of the three major task forces on injury control, heart disease prevention and nutrition; and in Volume 3, a series of commissioned papers. It was made commercially available to the public.**

AND SO TO THE FUTURE

Thus far, the implementation of the National Programme for Better Health has proved to be very difficult. Changing secretariat staff, new leadership and the weariness of long battles among many of the key players all tend to take their toll on the original conceptualisation and commitment.

There are precious few people in the health field capable of thinking in truly national strategic terms. It is as though we are asking for someone with the skills of an architect capable of grand and huge designs, who can re-think the entire shape and form of future cities, while most people in the architectural field plan little houses to a familiar suburban horizon. The lack of easy translation of the theoretical goals and targets into strategy has meant that great difficulties have followed for those working in the media supporting the Programme, because they have been unsure of how and to whom to pitch what message.

HEALTH FOR ALL, OR JUST FOR US?

It would be hard for me to discuss Health for All without mentioning my belief that Australia has some responsibility to assist in reorienting health care trans-nationally. It should not be forgotten that the Ottawa charter, which sets out the strategy for Health for All by the Year 2000, calls for international action for health.

Although the poorest in Australia live in virtually third world conditions, none of us comes from a region which is either as poor or as populous as South East Asia, India, Africa or Latin America. While we worry, and quite rightly so, about our internal problems of equity, 13 million children die each year in the developing world from largely preventable disorders. The city in which I live has 3 million people – fewer than are killed each year by the callous marketing of tobacco and breast milk substitutes.

Once we have signed up for something as idealistic as Health for All, there are certain moral imperatives related to these problems. They are, after all, our problems, as health professionals and as citizens of the countries which caused them. For make no mistake about it, the death and suffering in the underdeveloped world is not just a matter of brave little black people struggling to catch up with our clever industrial ways of doing things. It is our cigarette companies that have the bulk of the world market. It was the US which alone attempted to block the WHO's major policy initiative targetted at preventing the upwards of 10 per cent of all infant deaths which are caused by our companies marketing breast milk substitutes in the third world (a frightening case of non-medical provider dominance).

34

The issue of world health inequities is surely the most pressing need in reorienting health care systems, even though we can hardly be said to be reorienting it towards 'consumers' or 'patients' in developing countries where only 20 per cent of the population has access to primary health care. It is my hope that the Better Health Programme in Australia and its counterparts elsewhere will turn their attention to these issues before long.

The system we have, which feeds us health professionals so handsomely, is also the system which fails to come to grips with the lack of sanitation for most of the people in the world, or with the need for adequate care and pain relief for elderly people in our own communities. In the US, the system appears increasingly seduced by the promissory notes of molecular biology and transplantation, which have almost nothing to do with consumers' common health problems but everything to do with provider dominance.

Let no-one believe that the population cares not a fig for prevention with goals that affect the entire community. Go and ask them! Consumer groups with whom I mix in western Sydney (an underprivileged area within Australia) retain a commitment to and enthusiasm for prevention which would astonish many of my clinical and administrative colleagues. It beats the taste (especially the politics, fiscal arrangements and power-play) of modern medicine!

This paper has been rather savagely edited, and a full copy is available from the editor for those interested in the detail of the Better Health Commission.

National health: What is the focus?
(Editor)

There is an interesting confusion between 'The National Health' – which is shorthand in the United Kingdom for the National Health Care System – and the nation's health. All countries represented were struggling with what that means, and how and where it should be addressed. The twin notions of the health of the nation and the education of its citizens being the prime driving forces towards prosperity, peace and happiness seem like truisms, but only spasmodically are they translated into real action. As Ivan Illich noted many years ago,(1) it is possible to design systems which attempt to implement ideals which in fact make the situation worse.

All the five nations represented, except the United States, had some form of translation of the nation's health into a managed health care system. The roots for this lay in the British tradition, added to European notions of community and public provision. The United States, as was frequently discussed during the conference, is rooted far more in individualism, with both rights, responsibilities and fundamental notions of choice and freedom. This can include the 'choice' to have no health care or to take no care of your health.

We had in our possession the extensive and authoritative report on the view of the consumer in the United States towards health reform, produced by Louis Harris and Associates.(2) Major findings included:

● *a great reduction in satisfaction with the US system*

● *the likelihood that this dissatisfaction will continue to grow, particularly with reference to lack of cost control*

● *an increasing public pressure to do something about prices of hospitals and other provider institutions*

● *an aspiration that insurance should cover more – surprisingly 62 per cent of Americans seemed to be willing to pay a small amount to help cover the famous 35 million or so people who have little or no cover.*

There are many other important points; anyone interested in the future of American healthcare would find this an intriguing document – like

---

(1) Illich, Ivan. Limits to Medicine. Open Forum 1976.
(2) Hospital Strategic Outlook. *The Public*. Louis Harris and Associates 1990.

many surveys, however, the responses are sometimes mutually contradicting.

The basic American position in our discussions seemed to be that 'something had to be done', supported beyond the usual limits of liberal opinion, but no one was clear exactly what that 'something' would be. It was also unclear in what forum or place the decision could be made. This is in contrast, of course, to all the other systems represented in which State and/or Federal governments have a specific role in determining the overall structure. Since the 1993 election, President CLinton has determined that 'it will be done' and done by his wife.

This provided an interesting policy and strategic background. For every good suggestion, there were always a series of reasons why it would not or could not work. The following paper from Ed Connors takes the perspective of one of the players in this debate, namely the American Hospitals Association. What follows is greatly shortened from the original. In terms of our model, no one could claim that the responses were quick. However, there has emerged a much greater flexibility and a willingness to join together various pieces. In turn, an overall system to eradicate the most glaring inequalities and to help check spiralling costs can grow. In other words, a clearer focus can speed up and move existing systems.

TOWARD THE DEVELOPMENT OF A NATIONAL HEALTHCARE STRATEGY

ED CONNORS (UNITED STATES)

INTRODUCTION

This paper sets out some actions by the American Hospital Association to develop a plan to reform the system of financing and delivery of health services in the United States. The paper provides related and selective information from the perceived perspective of providers, payers and patients on the current thinking in the United States on the need for reform and its content.

PROVIDERS OF CARE

The American Hospital Association has a well developed system of policy formulation and advocacy and excellent data on policy issues. We recently undertook an extensive process to re-examine how the health system might be improved – timely in view of widespread concern about features of our health system and the likelihood of serious debate, and probably action, in reforming it.

The first step of the process has been a sobering assessment of the problems facing the field, what I have grouped under five headings.

1. Access

An unacceptably high and growing number of individuals and families fall through the gaps of the private/public system of health care financing.

The willingness and ability of employers, particularly small employers, to offer private health insurance as an employee benefit has been eroded by the cost of health benefits and cost shifting from public to private purchasers and within the private sector.

Constraints on government resources have led to efforts to control the rate of increase in spending on health care by restricting eligibility and provider payment under public programmes such as Medicare and Medicaid.

38

Changes in delivery patterns and demography are creating a need for long term care that cannot be met by existing resources or capacity and for which adequate financing is unavailable.

Uneven access to health care services is exacerbated by geographic maldistribution of health care facilities and professionals together with a lack of adequate capacity in some localities.

2. Cost-effectiveness

● A level of uncertainty concerning efficacy, effectiveness, cost-benefits of treatment;

● the absence of consensus within society at large as to what represents appropriate limits of treatment;

● unlimited patient expectations;

● potential tort liability; and

● the absence of social consensus on difficult personal and ethical choices.

3. Individual responsibility

Incentives do not encourage individuals to adapt personal behaviour to improve their own health or to use health care services effectively.

4. Value/quality

Quality, to the extent that it is measurable, appears to vary widely across providers.

Providers lack the means of demonstrating either the quality of the care they provide, the reasonableness of their costs/prices, or the consequences for access and quality of reductions in costs/prices.

Consumers and purchasers are not able to make informed decisions based on the value of services received (that is, cost in relation to quality) under alternative delivery and financing arrangements, or to hold providers accountable for the quality or cost of the care they provide.

Patients or consumers, purchasers, and providers cannot arrive at agreement concerning what to provide, to whom or under what conditions, at what cost/price.

5. Financing and management

Widely varying mechanisms for administering insurance benefits are costly and confusing to everyone involved: patients, providers and purchasers.

Methods and levels of payment and the absence of patient insurance increasingly subject hospitals and other providers to unmanageable risks affecting future financial viability, reducing the ability of providers to manage.

Financial incentives and the organisation of the delivery system encourage the provision of acute care rather than prevention of disease or management of chronic conditions to prevent acute episodes.

Hospitals, physicians, and other providers work under differing and often conflicting or perverse incentives.

The nature of incentives and the fragmentation of delivery systems can lead, in certain instances, to duplication of technology and capacity by hospitals and other providers within a community, service levels beyond those necessary, and attempts to shift responsibility for costs and quality onto someone else.

These problems are viewed as real, serious and worthy of attention by all segments of society. Accordingly, the American Hospital Association has agreed on a set of criteria with which to guide their own health care reform plan and to use it in evaluating the plans and initiatives of others.

The criteria adopted by the Association are based on three principles:

1. reform should build on the strengths of the pluralistic health care delivery and financing system that has evolved over the past 50 years;

2. reform should be designed to meet the needs of communities and patients; and

3. reform may entail substantial change in delivery and financing arrangements.

What distinguishes a pluralistic system from a centralised or unitary system is the possibility of diversity in ownership, delivery arrangements and the impact that may have on both public and private financing.

Restrictions on benefits would be related to the different payers' willingness and ability to pay, allowing for diversity between, and even within, the public and private sectors. Finally, different provider payment methods could be operative within and across the public and private sectors.

It is important to note however, full diversity is not a prerequisite for a pluralistic system. Pluralism need not pertain in all areas. One could opt for centralised financing and pluralistic delivery.

Criterion A: Essential and basic services available to all.

Criterion B: High quality, that is, co-ordination of care among providers and across levels of care; continuity of care over time or between episodes of illness; improvement of outcome through diffusion and appropriate use of innovations in both technology and medical practice; delivery of effective care only; the use of the most cost-effective treatment to manage a patient's condition; monitoring of practice and constructive peer review to identify improvements in practice.

Criterion C: Adequately and fairly financed between private risk and public good. The outcome for the provider should be fair and adequate payment for services delivered.

Criterion D: Affordable. Patients and their purchasers should be able to select benefits and delivery arrangements that emphasise 'value' by enabling them to obtain the kind of care for which they are willing and able to pay. Based on the availability of funds, public programmes for those not able to finance their own care should explicitly limit access to care beyond 'basic care' by restricting benefits or choice of provider.

Criterion E: Efficiently delivered. Continuous improvement in the efficient use of resources to restore or preserve health. Financial incentives to encourage individuals to adopt healthy lifestyles and responsibly use health services.

Criterion F: Community-focused/patient centred. Management at local level: community variation in medical practice; fostering appropriate expectations for care; treating all patients with dignity and courtesy.

The paper continued with an identification of similar concerns expressed by Blue Cross/Blue Shield/representatives of business and industry, organised labour and public opinion and then concludes.

Clearly, from the selected references offered in this paper, a reform mood characterises the American health care scene. No one is satisfied with the status quo.

Federal action is anticipated after our recent presidential election (1992) and is unlikely to take place then if the deficit problem facing our federal government is not on the road to solution through a combination of spending cuts and increased taxes.

The content of the reform is speculative at this point. It is my personal belief that we are moving in a direction which will have the following features of a reformed health care system.

- All Americans will have health insurance. Employers will be mandated to cover employees and their dependents. The mandated coverage will include benefits similar to the current Medicare benefits.

- The Federal government will finance health insurance for all not covered as a result of workplace insurance to include elderly and unemployed people. The financing will be through a broadly based dedicated tax.

- Both government and private insurers will require changes in the delivery of health care as a condition of payment.

- Integration of hospitals, physicians and other providers into comprehensive health care delivery organisations with responsibility for a defined (enrolled) population will emerge and ultimately be required as a condition of payment.

- These new comprehensive delivery organisations will be not-for-profit, governed by community leaders, capable of accepting financial risk for delivering all needed care to a defined population and regulated through our State's government. Cost increases will be constrained through such regulation on an annual global budget ceiling mechanism. Thus, regulated 'competition' will result. Competing, comprehensive, health delivery organisations will compete for enrollees to 'their' system and, thus, will meet consumer expectations as well as meeting government (State) regulations. About 75 per cent of Americans will have an annual choice of enrolling in a competing system. The remaining 25 per cent will be those who live in sparsely populated areas unable to support two competing 'systems' of care.

This direction seems the most likely American response to the complex challenges of access, quality and affordability.

What happens if the public is satisfied? (Editor)

It is generally recognised that most Canadians are satisfied with their health care system. It is fairly expensive, in GNP terms, certainly compared to the United Kingdom, although considerably less so than its close neighbour. Some argue that the per capita spend of around 10 per cent is about 'right'. During the conference, delegates moved away from the sense of complacency that this could engender into asking hard questions about the purpose and effectiveness of their system. What emerged from their deliberations, particularly working as a group on the final day of our seminar, was the need for individual managers and politicians to change their focus. As soon as one stops considering individual interactions between clinicians and their patients, or the specific facilities which exist and operate and looks instead at the needs of the nation, then notions of satisfaction will also move.

Throughout the conference, and not simply relating to Canada, there was much discussion about how far threatening external environments were necessary in order to move organisations forward – a form of 'force majeure'. In all publicly funded systems, the problems of budget deficits and economic difficulties, which have subsequently increased in all five nations, would clearly be seen as such external stimuli.

The following brief extract sets out these issues together.

HOW MUCH IS ENOUGH?

MARIE FORTIER (CANADA)

Recent Canadian federal deficit reduction policies have placed limits on the rate of growth of the federal share of funding, thereby increasing pressure on provincial governments. Faced with a public debt of $363 billion at the end of 1989-90 (over 50 per cent of GDP), and an annual deficit of $30 million (4.7 per cent of GDP), the federal government decided to adopt an Expenditure Control Plan.

Provincial governments gather and allocate resources, and operate the health care system. In Canada, provincial governments have been faced with increasing costs due to advancing technology, increased population awareness and expectations, and reduced funding due to restrictions on federal transfer payments and economic slow down. The range of options available to provinces is not unlimited. After all, there are only two sides to the ledger: revenue and expenses. The first option is to increase taxes directly, an unpopular move at any time but even more so in a less than flourishing economic climate and therefore one that would encounter much resistance from the electorate.

The second option is to increase taxes indirectly by excluding services from insurance coverage or charging special fees for certain services.

The third option is a reduction of services either globally or selectively; some argue (providers and patients) that this is precisely how provincial governments have been handling the situation: reduced hospital budgets leading to temporary or permanent bed closures, or the deliberate use of acute care beds for long term care patients (bed blockers) consuming fewer resources than would acute patients; rationing measures designed to limit the volume of services available and create queues.

The fourth option is for provinces to review their current health care system and try to identify new areas where improvement in the efficiency and effectiveness of health services would yield desired impacts on the cost of health care while improving or at least maintaining the current health status of the population.

The federal government does not exercise any management role over this system. Its role is limited to a single factor: transfer payments. Proponents of a larger federal role argue that the accessibility requirements of the Canada Health Act could be used to direct the organisation of health services by provinces (where and in what form services are available). The federal government does not subscribe to that position.

44

PROVIDERS

Providers are health professionals, and organisations (community and institutional) as well as voluntary agencies. Whether individually or as groups, they have the option to fight the payers, and may do so privately or publicly. Physicians' and nurses' strikes have occurred sporadically in Canada in the last 20 years though it can be argued that each case is unique and can only be understood in its own peculiar context. Hospital associations are well organised lobbies and have had some success in influencing governments in the past. Among providers, some claim that the health system is experiencing a crisis and call for increased funding and availability of services as the only solutions. Some providers, perhaps realising that increased funding is not forthcoming, choose to collaborate on fine tuning the system, in order to wring every dollar for maximum effect while keeping their eye on quality of care. Indeed, utilisation management programmes combined with good management practices have achieved success in spite of sporadic medical resistance. There is, however, an increasing willingness on the part of provider groups to change from the confrontation mode to the collaborative mode in their dealings with each other and with governments.

Some of these solutions focus on the continuing conflict between two opposing funding systems which providers have acknowledged for a long time. The institutional sector is funded through a global budget while physicians, considered the gatekeepers of the system, are still mainly remunerated on a fee-for-service basis. Interesting research work under way may open new possibilities well beyond case-mix groupings. The concept of linking payment of hospital and physician services on the basis of appropriateness of admission and treatment, and satisfactory outcome (relative to reasonable expectation) has never been tested in Canada. Several current research streams may lay the groundwork necessary for such experimentation.

PATIENTS

Patients and their relatives also have the option to lobby individually or as organised groups. There exists a number of patient advocacy groups who pressure government for increased attention to their health problem, though there is no overall patient advocacy movement in Canada. There are public outcries in cases of highly publicised deaths on waiting lists leading some patients to seek medical and hospital care out of their province or out of the country. This, however, is not possible for the vast majority of Canadians.

45

Ethical issues are gaining prominence and members of the public are more and more engaged in debating them, and at times provoking debate. In Canada, most groups lobbying for services do so at the provincial level. Some health issues take national prominence because of their seriousness, because of the role of the federal government in protecting the health of Canadians or because the federal government itself chooses to take the lead.

CONCLUSION

Budgetary restraint is forcing a review of resource allocation and, thus, a refocus on desired outcome. Without it, it may not have happened.

What's in it for me?
(Editor)

If we move from the idea of focusing on a whole nation and system to the individuals who will have to make the changes and adaptations, some interesting questions arise. In particular, the one thing which links the often uncertain, bewildering and frequently crass field of motivation studies is the notion of incentive. This term has been stolen by the early theorists who developed it into piece rates or payment by results, which still refuses to die, despite overwhelming evidence of its uselessness in most modern society. The idea of intrinsic motivation, that satisfaction is obtained from doing the job well, is often lost. (*) A key result of this is that where there are existing financial and direct incentives, organisations must make choices. It can be very time consuming to dismantle them, moving managerial energy into confrontations and struggles which may not, in the short term, be particularly productive. The second choice, probably a transitional one, is to ensure that such incentives are in harmony with the real goals of the organisation and are not acting as perverse incentives. A perverse incentive, that most interesting notion, is one which causes somebody to do something new, or additional, or more, or sometimes less, but where it is the opposite or at least not the same as what was wanted. So, in law and order systems, you

---

(*) This comment will anger some senior United Kingdom health managers who have introduced an elegant system of performance-related pay. I can find no evidence that it achieves what it is supposed to.

46

can encourage the police by offering incentives for arrests or apprehension of speeding motorists. It is likely that more arrests will occur, but whether of the right people, or for appropriate offences for police concern, given the opportunity cost involved, is always questionable. Indeed, although another story, the best health care system would be one which did itself out of business, (as originally anticipated in the heady days of the inception of the NHS) not one which could point to ever more interventions and patient days.

The next paper takes us from the general notion into the particular, concerning the medical profession. This is made more interesting than the usual debate about incentives because of the intrusion and overlap into clinical freedom and so, ultimately, into rationing and who makes resource allocation decisions.

THE AUTONOMY OF THE MEDICAL PROFESSION MUST BE EARNED

KEN FYKE (CANADA)

This contribution pays attention to the need – obvious when stated simply – to ensure that incentive and payment systems are in line with the focus of the organisation. The author enters the area of clinical freedom, which also featured throughout the conference as part of provider dominance. In particular, he notes:

> *Autonomy is not a right of professionals, nor a prerequisite to being a professional. It is a social reward, exchanged in recognition of the professionals' pursuit of knowledge for the purpose of better service to others. Professional autonomy is granted when society can trust practitioners to pursue goals which are consistent with the greater good of society.*

He argues that there is a difference between professional behaviour and autonomy:

> *The distinction between professional behaviour and autonomy is clear when the underlying values are considered. The profession values self-determination and society values physicians' commitment to helping others. These values are the roots of the professional behaviour. In contrast, professional autonomy may actually threaten patient care.*

The nature of physician reimbursement in Canada has, according to Ken Fyke, led to a situation where physicians can specialise, earn generous incomes in hospital practice, and have a great deal of autonomy. He then outlines the difficulty of spiralling health care costs, the absence of any control over physician reimbursement, and places this in the context of inadequate measures of the quality of outcomes. Given that the patients may now be aware and rightly concerned that the care they receive may be unnecessary or harmful, the paper goes on to discuss how the issues of fee incentives, professional autonomy and standards of care can be linked.

(Editor)

48

Why must professional fee incentives be linked to standards?

Professional behaviour, rather than autonomy, is the essential factor in attaining social benefit. It requires scientifically based standards to ensure that medical practitioners will translate medical standards into practice. I am proposing that two approaches be simultaneously applied: a) professional involvement and b) linking financial incentives to medical standards.

Information produced on outcomes of care (subsequently translated into medical standards), must be acted on actually to improve medical practice. The literature Chassin (1) has reviewed shows that simple transmission of information about standards is not enough to produce significant and lasting improvement. Results are improved if the process of developing a standard involves the consensus of esteemed professionals, an acceptable body issues the standard and writes it clearly. To be successfully accepted, standards should be written with input from credible physicians, researchers and other health care professionals where appropriate.

The process of entrenching standards for practice will need financial reinforcement to change practice patterns. In other words, once interventions of marginal or no clinical benefit are established, or patient indicators that do not warrant intervention emerge, funding of the unwarranted treatment must not continue. Further, payers may use such indicators to determine the appropriateness of waiting lists, and decide whether or not to re-allocate funds to them. Standards do not amount to 'cook book' medicine, or rationing, provided professionals involve themselves in the process of developing them, and provided these standards allow for the state of the art in therapies that are less clear-cut or developed than others.

Still further, relating fee schedules to accepted standards of care can protect the incomes of physicians who practise medicine appropriately and keep their knowledge current. Standards for care and outcome can support informed decision-making by the patient.

Linking financial rewards provides the incentive for the physician to spend the time sharing information and assisting the client to problem solve and decide on the appropriate care for him or herself.

(1) Chassin, Mark R. Standards of care in medicine. Inquiry 25 1988 (437-453).

CONCLUSION

In summary, the development of nationally accepted guidelines to clinical practice, based on professional consensus and evaluation of treatment outcomes, will protect professional autonomy from outside regulation. This strategy, as opposed to regulation, will better serve the interests of patients. Care will benefit from the medical profession's collective experience and from clients and physicians interacting in decision making. Medicine will never be absolutely clear-cut because in the end the patient must weigh the risks and benefits and decide what is appropriate. No professional can completely fulfil this role.

I think the medical profession will support this strategy even though its practice patterns will be challenged, provided this occurs on the grounds of scientific evidence and in a nurturing peer environment. The integrity and work of the profession's body of knowledge determines the physician's individual and collective value to society. Therefore, it is this base that must be established to protect the profession's autonomy. In this sense, physicians are hampered by the medical uncertainty that undermines their ability to benefit their patients. I think physicians will welcome the assistance of their colleagues, particularly those in academic medicine, as they struggle to maintain the integrity of their profession and to restore public confidence in the efficacy and social merit of their service.

Financial rewards related to this professional consensus provide the final incentive to physicians to practice appropriate medicine. Neither the development of standards for practice nor changes to the fee schedule require that control be taken from the profession, nor do they threaten medical innovation. These strategies will in fact promote innovation, discourage ineffective practices and restore society's trust and confidence.

The old stories are the best
(Editor)

Health care is adorned with pious hopes and statements of intent. 'The patient comes first', we shout: 'health care is a right': 'needs not wants should drive the system': 'primary and community care deliver to more people than acute services and should be appropriately funded': 'health promotion and illness prevention are important concepts'. The list is endless, but the reality following analysis in all countries is that these aspirations are not being put into effective action – (the implementation gap already discussed). It is also because no-one has discovered how to make the radical changes in perception and behaviour that all these statements require. That kind of new focus is quite frightening and it is easy for all of us to shy away, make the pious statement and assume that if we say something often enough it may possibly happen.

The next paper picks up one such 'hope' – the move from acute to community – and looks at the realities of a hospital in Australia trying to achieve this. Along the way, the author discovers some interesting things about resource allocation decisions and the real difficulty of translating such decisions into actions. As this is a scene which all our systems must increasingly face, the lessons contained here are illuminating.

SETTING GOALS AND TARGETS FOR BETTER HEALTH: REORIENTATING THE HEALTHCARE SYSTEM TOWARDS CONSUMER HEALTH

JENNIFER ALEXANDER (AUSTRALIA)

White settlement in Australia began with the arrival of the First Fleet in 1788 at Sydney Harbour. Sydney, the capital city of the State of New South Wales, now has a population of almost 4 million. Its characteristic suburban sprawl stretches from the shores of the Harbour in the east to the Blue Mountains, some 40 to 50 kilometres away to the west. The population remains mixed with a high proportion of new arrivals still settling in Sydney.

As is common in many cities around the world, hospitals and other health facilities were established in the parts of Sydney settled first, and the provision of health care facilities has failed to keep up with population growth. Eastward expansion of Sydney is limited by the Pacific Ocean. Australians have moved north, west and southwards to build their homes, usually described as 'the Australian dream on a quarter acre block'. This paper will focus on health services in parts of western Sydney.

In 1963 the then Chairman of the Hospitals Commission of NSW, reported to Parliament that:

> *The modern general hospital extends its own activities beyond its own four walls by the provision of such activities as rehabilitation services, follow-up clinics, and home-care programmes.*

Twenty-five years later, many writers now agree that the hospital of the future will reach out into homes and residential communities as much as it depends on the sick to cross its threshold for help. In 20 years, health care will be concentrated in the home and in the residential community, not on the hospital campus.

The development of community health services in western Sydney provides an opportunity to review the lessons of that twenty-five year period. Hopefully, these lessons may assist us to shape the future in the best interests of those we hope to serve. Indeed, the history of the community health services of western Sydney is particularly relevant to the theme of this seminar, for it is the story of a payer initiative of the early 1970s, which, even at that stage, created tensions between health care providers.

Within the framework of this paper simple definitions of payer, provider and patient will be used, based on who pays for, who produces and who receives 'health' goods. In the Australian context payers may be federal or State governments and medical insurance companies. Funding for community health services is totally a government issue. Providers include all health professionals giving services to patients. The patient may be an individual, a family or the community.

WESTMEAD HOSPITAL

In 1988 the provision of health services to the population of western Sydney became the responsibility of the Western Sydney Area Health Service (WSAHS), covering a population of approximately 650,000.

WSAHS determined that the community health services operating in three local government districts (covering a population of 310,000) would be administered as part of a single organisational unit – the Westmead and Parramatta Hospitals and Community Health Services. The two hospitals operate as a single unit, though they are physically separate. Westmead Hospital is the major tertiary referral hospital for WSAHS.

At that time a new division was established within the administrative structure of Westmead Hospital, and a director of community health services was appointed. Prior to this appointment, community health services were the responsibility of Westmead Hospital's Community Medicine Department. This earlier arrangement was not seen as satisfactory by the parties involved. Community Medicine was part of the Medical Services division, and many in Community Health believed that the aims of Community Medicine (needs identification, strategic development and evaluation) were at odds with the objectives of Community Health. Provider tension had reared its head!

In 1990, the WSAHS commissioned a review of its community health services. This report outlined the services available through each main centre and the target population of the service. Without providing a specific definition, the report attempted to describe the characteristics of a community health service. These they described as:

- A multidisciplinary approach to specific health problems.

- An holistic view of the causes and treatment of health problems.

- A willingness and ability to adapt the delivery of health services to changing health needs. (This contrasts with a service direction dictated by professional fashion.)

- An aim to prevent inappropriate institutionalisation or use of specialist care.

- Providing an accessible point of contact and referral to the larger health system.

- An acceptance of responsibility for the well being of a total resident population.

- The inter-sectoral approach.

- Illness prevention and health promotion.

Further, it stated that:

> *Community Health Services are not solely an extension of the curative process begun in hospitals although post-discharge functions are an important component of the work. In fact, the majority of community health service clients have little or no contact with institutional care and when some ... do it is a minor episode in the total continuation of care provided by a health service.*

The core community health services have been identified as:

- counselling

- early detection and screening

- geriatric and disabled persons day care

- speech, occupational and physiotherapy

- health education and promotion

- dental services.

Despite the community health services being the focus of this paper it would be wrong to leave the reader with the impression that these services describe the full extent of community involvement of the Westmead Hospital organisation.

There are now five distinct forces under the general 'banner' of 'community' health services, as follows:

1. Community health

2. Community medicine

3. The Department of General Practice

4. Specialty Outreach Services

5. Health promotion

Several points of discussion emerge relevant to the theme of the seminar.

Sources of tension – providers

1. There is no consensus regarding the most appropriate model for the provision of community health services and, indeed, there may be several different 'missions' under the same banner.

2. Issues of professional rivalries and reputations inevitably find their way into this type of debate. For many years, community health has been seen, and indeed within community health many have seen it, as anti-institution and anti-medical. In some quarters these rivalries are quite polarised. Consequently, the different parties have very little knowledge of the nature of services currently provided by the other and great trust has been required from both sides where the gulf has been bridged. Bridging the gap is a major issue for management.

3. Apart from philosophical issues associated with the nature of health and how health services should be provided, there are also concerns, particularly in some areas of community health, about the potential threat to career structures and professional autonomy. Because of the history of their development, community health services have separate career structures and reporting relationships from hospital based services. Indeed, the linking of community health with the hospital based services, as has occurred at Westmead, has not occurred everywhere.

4. Additional to the debate outlined above is a debate within community health itself regarding generalist versus specialist services. The original model developed within the western region was based on generalist community nurses providing primary care to a known population group. The Community Health Programme (CHP) was, in practice, set up as a two-tier system – generalists as the first tier, and a second tier of 'specialist' back-up. The specialists included psychologists, social workers, speech, occupational and physiotherapists. The two-tier system was basically a generalist service, focused to meet the needs of their geographically defined population. Over time, some specialisation of services has developed, such as mental health teams.

5. The initial description of the plan for the CHP included primary care teams supporting and 'surrounding' the local general medical practitioner, with the initial introduction of a local generalist community nurse (GCN). These GCN positions still exist in the Community Health Programme administered by Westmead Hospital.

   In most areas the medical profession strongly opposed the introduction of the CHP and, by and large, individual medical practitioners did not become part of the team. This lack of medical involvement from the start in the provision of community health services has had several consequences. The CHPs have been perceived as having a non-medical bias in the services provided and, indeed, some community health workers have, at times, voiced strong anti-medical sentiments.

   An additional factor which may continue to foster this debate could result from the fact that, since the early 1970s, the CHP has offered a separate career path for nursing and allied health professionals. Some of those who established the CHP in the 1970s have not been associated with hospitals since that time. Hence, they may be less aware of significant developments in hospitals in the use of multidisciplinary teams and the greater awareness of all the social issues that surround a patient (or client), apart from the single illness episode. Conversely, hospital staff have had little opportunity to participate in the community health services. Attempts at rotating staff between community health and hospitals have usually been unsuccessful, or at the most of limited value.

6. The CHP was a payer initiative of the Federal government of the early 1970s. 'Payer' initiatives are still alive and well, and, in some instances, overriding locally determined requirements.

7. The potential for tension between the payers and the providers is particularly well illustrated in the area of financing of health services provided to the community. Westmead and Parramatta Hospitals and community health services have an operating budget of approximately $M200 (Australian). This is divided into four main programmes: Drug and Alcohol Services, Inpatient and Outpatient Services, Mental Health Services (inpatient, outpatient, community) and Geriatric Services.

   The total community health funding is comprised of components of all four programmes listed above. In addition, within each of these components, funding may be specifically identified for certain services, this funding having been provided from either State or Federal governments. The byzantine nature of the funding for community health services only adds to the complexities of planning a comprehensive service and the difficulties of making decisions regarding resource allocation.

8. Of particular concern is the marginal approach adopted by many funding sources. Funds may be provided for the delivery of a service, the nature of which may have been determined outside the organisation. This funding usually provides for the additional marginal costs only, assuming the provision of an infrastructure from existing resources. On a small scale, provision of marginal costs may be justified but, when multiple programmes are involved, such an approach provides, in itself, an additional resource demand. The organisation may have no choice but to maintain and support the services and that requirement may divert resources away from existing services.

   Both payers and providers may be found 'guilty' of the sin of 'marginality'. In developing proposals for funding some providers request only the marginal costs, and even these may be minimised in order to make the request appear more 'appealing' for funding.

9. Patients – within the area much attention is being given to the identification of the health needs of the population and the development of appropriate services to meet these needs. Under the Area Health legislation, WSAHS is responsible for meeting the health needs of the population including the promotion of services to maintain health as well as the provision of services to restore the health of individuals. Attention is inevitably drawn to the issue of individual versus population-based health services: who is the patient – the individual or the community? In very general terms the five types of community services outlined above can be categorised as:

Health Promotions – population
Community Health – mixed individual and population
Community Medicine – population
Specialty Outreach – individual
General Practice – individual

What is not clear is the extent to which these different foci define very different services, and the extent to which it is possible to operate services, serving two different notions of 'patients' within a single entity.

10. Despite the increasing debate regarding the allocation of scarce health resources, parameters for the distribution of society's resources have yet to be defined. Economists and ethicists discuss utilitarian, Rawlsian and other models of distributive justice. While well developed in an economic sense, such models are rarely discussed in the political debates surrounding the funding of renal units or geriatric care services. The theories of the equitable distribution of scarce resources have rarely been applied specifically in health. Indeed, the issue of what is equity in health and health care remains confused. The notion of an individual's right to health care is still very dominant in Australia. While a population of patients with AIDS or renal disease might be discussed within the debate, such discussions still basically focus on the individual as a patient, and the marginal increase in resources to meet an identified need (usually not described as a demand). Given the complexity of the debate, the notion of comprising the individual with the community at large in determining the allocation of resources has usually only surfaced where the two components are both clearly defined. Should the additional marginal resources be allocated to treat this child with whooping cough or should the resources be allocated to increase the availability of whooping cough immunisation in the community?

The health services provided to the individual patient are essentially private goods (whether privately or publicly provided). In contrast, the health services provided to the community (that is, the community as the 'patient') are really public goods, perhaps exhibiting some features of partial congestion (for example, in the limitation of class sizes for health education). Some community focused or public health goods are 'pure' public goods (for example, environmental protection), some are private goods with large externalities (for example, immunisation) and other private merit goods (for example, behaviour modification classes). The juxtaposition of these two types of goods in the decision regarding the allocation of resources, compounds even further an already complex debate.

58

The two types of goods operate within different time frames (cure now, prevent for the future), and, in many instances, the outcome for the interventions has not been evaluated.

While considerable insight has been gained into the normative rules that would guide an all-knowing and Pareto-optimising government, in the real world decision-makers face near insurmountable problems. The combined properties of joint consumption and non-excludability prevent the market price mechanism from being used to determine the preferences of individuals for marginal changes in public goods output (even assuming that the individuals themselves have enough information to make an assessment).

11. The theory of public choice in the allocation of public goods (as distinct from private goods in which the market price mechanism plays a role in allocation) centres on the voting process as the means 'by which the preferences of individuals for public goods are rationally transmitted to policy matters'.

    Economists define a social welfare function as 'a representation of the preference-ordering for society over alternative resource allocations.' The resource allocation applies to both the 'combination of commodities produced, and a distribution of those commodities over consumers'. They discuss concepts such as vertical equity (that is, how the system treats individuals of differing welfare levels) and horizontal equity (that is, treating equals equally).

    The decision maker in public decision has to ascertain the preference of those on whose behalf he is making the decision. This is the first important difference between public and private resource allocations.

    In the private market, the firm does not have to balance the claims and interests of one group against those of another .... decisions are made on an individual basis. In contrast, in the public sector, decisions are made collectively.

    The problem of reconciling differences arises wherever there must be a collective decision. Popular political discussions often refer to what the 'people' want. But since different people want different things, how, out of these divergent views, can a social decision be made?

Much is written about the need to consult the consumer, the community, when making decisions regarding the allocation of health resources and deciding on the nature of the services to be provided. As shown above, academic economists have demonstrated the practical difficulties in application. Some economists are now testing the long held assumption that consumers will never reveal their true preference for public goods and that they will always see that it is in their interest to 'free ride'. Some techniques have been developed to determine the true consumer preference for a public good. In other areas, survey methodology has been used and could be useful for the examination of major issues. Some means must be found to involve the consumers in the decisions regarding the nature and distribution of health resources. Such involvement may well develop new tensions between the 'patients' (individuals or the 'community') and the providers, the traditional determiners of service provision.

CONCLUSION

The history of the development of the community health services in western Sydney shows that payer initiatives in determining the way health services are delivered have been in operation for decades already, and that they still exist. Also shown has been the fact that the way in which a policy initiative is eventually implemented may differ considerably from the original intent. This may be for a variety of reasons including changes in who is the payer, altered funding levels and the intervention of the health care providers themselves. This issue has been commented upon by Young and Saltman:

> Made at some central level (national, regional province, state or whatever), much of what actually happens in the way of resource distribution takes place via decisions at much lower levels of the delivery system, frequently at the individual patient level. The resulting need to achieve a high degree of co-ordination between the planning and control functions has proved to be extremely difficult to attain.

Young and Saltman continue:

> Pluralist systems appear to be almost inherently unable to impose even basic types of linkage between planning decisions (whether at national or regional levels) and operating behaviour, particularly for large expensive institutions like hospitals.

Focus – organisational goals and the value problem
(Editor)

A common issue in our represented countries is summarised loosely in the term 'values'. While we accept the need for focus and effective organisation and management to ensure the attainment of any vision, it is all too easy to ignore legitimate differences in values.

Equally, it is easy to find examples of values and moral principles being used to obscure the need for action, or to avoid it altogether. Managers within the complicated parts of the economy have to balance the tension between real, legitimate and deeply-held values which prevent individuals or groups from working towards certain kinds of change and people simply blocking. An additional difficulty for managers and decision-makers arises when there is demand for user or consumer values, not only to be heard and represented, but also to become much more dominant. Beyond provider dominance can lie user dominance.

The extracts which follow illustrate some of these issues in two different national contexts.

THE ROLE OF VALUES

KAREN POUTASI (NEW ZEALAND)

As a manager who would rather get on with fixing a system and making it work, I am a reluctant convert to the particular theme of this paper. The reality of health care requires an understanding of the values held by key players and the reality of managing requires the ability to achieve some balance in those values. New Zealand, along with other countries, is attempting to determine what quality and efficiency gains can be achieved by balancing the conflicting interests of payers, providers and users and managing changes in the various power bases.

'Beyond provider dominance' reflects the existence of a prevailing system which characterised the New Zealand health care system until the 1980s. 'Provider capture' is a well-worn term. Given the peculiarities of health care which result in a significant imbalance of information between users and providers, this phenomenon was not surprising. Nor was it necessarily to the disadvantage of the user. Indeed, when we consider the market model of incomplete vertical integration in the health care industry, elements of provider dominance are inevitable. The variable is magnitude rather than presence or absence. A familiar situation in health care markets has most exchanges taking place between transactors who are not independent or at arms length to each other and yet who are not under common ownership or management either. Their interests are partially shared and partially conflicting. The values that providers bring to the relationship have been weighted by the medical monopoly of health care provision. This monopoly is now being challenged by management, for example, through the move to more complete vertical integration within area health boards. It was previously challenged by other providers, notably nurses, but medical socialisation has brought with it values which range from altruism through paternalism to profit seeking.

If we turn to users, we can see that they value dignity and that they may have concerns not shared by the provider. Acceptability is a value that users are emphasising as increasingly important. In New Zealand, Maori users of our system question whether their cultural values will respected. While providers become more and more specialised, users are focusing on health as a complete state of physical, mental, spiritual and social well-being – and an issue that goes well beyond the health care system itself. It is notoriously difficult to measure this value. 'Willingness to pay' is a measure, but is, of course, not always matched by ability to pay. This introduces the payers into the field of play. The users hope that the values of the payers will mirror their own values, and that they will act as advocates for them.

Users are likely to value accessibility to a comprehensive range of quality services when ill, a safe environment and support in adopting and maintaining healthy lifestyles. Users also place value on the security of knowing that, in the event of sudden catastrophic illness or accident, they can receive quality medical care without confronting a barrier of significant costs. They may self-insure or be prepared to pay taxes to ensure access to a public health system. Users value personal health outcomes. The other players, of course, do also, but users have the most invested in their own health.

From a manager's point of view, therefore, there is and will always be a need to recognise values. Providers may be displaced by users or payers in terms of apparent dominance, or by different sets of provider relationships. Whatever unfolds, it is the manager who will 'hold the ring'.

Within any present or future system, equity can be seen to win almost universal approval as an objective in health care. However one defines equity, it has something to do with justice. Most would accept this as an appropriate value for public payer, acting on behalf of users and applying it to the distributive resource mechanisms. However, equity, like health itself, is a value-laden concept which has no uniquely correct definition. So, do public payers value equity of access, equity of health, or equity of health care consumption? We can argue strongly for an explicit definition in order to close the gap between principle and practice. It may help both managers and key players if we can struggle with some of these concepts and begin to produce definitions which are operable and which can actually be used to measure policy and action alongside.

Everything should be made as simple as possible, but not more so.
Albert Einstein

A practical view of changing values
(Editor)

Jo Boufford, who has a long experience in managing the public hospital system in the United States, looks at the practicalities of changing the focus of the organisation. As she points out, the current focus of most health care delivery systems is on the transaction between the institutional and individual provider and the individual patient. In line with some of the changing values, already noted in Karen Poutasi's paper, and the notion of empowerment of users in communities, it is interesting to follow her discussion of what would happen were this to become a reality rather than an ideal. In particular, she discusses the specific likely changes in the behaviour of payers, patients and providers, and suggests some of the key considerations of any policy maker moving in this direction. It is particularly topical in the context of changing values in the United States and the recognition that 'something must be done' under the new Clinton administration.

She provides a neat conclusion to the section, drawing together the grand issues of overall organisation focus, of values, acceptance of empowerment and the necessary adaptations that all these changing views require.

SHIFTING THE FOCUS FROM THE INDIVIDUAL PATIENT TO THE COMMUNITY

JO BOUFFORD (UNITED STATES AND THE KING'S FUND COLLEGE)

INTRODUCTION

There is considerable dynamism in the relationships, among payers, providers and patients, especially with the introduction or modification of market forces. Nevertheless, the organisation structure, financing and regulation of most health care delivery systems are almost completely focused on the transaction between the institutional (hospital, long term care facility or organised primary care practice), or individual provider and the individual patient, and how to control the cost and maximise the quality of that transaction. In public health terms this might be called a numerator oriented health care delivery system – responding to the needs and demands of those who present for care.

A health care delivery system in which the community is seen as the patient/consumer is a very different concept; a shift to a 'denominator focus' that goes beyond the needs and demands of the users of the delivery system and looks at those of the population (or community) of which the individual patient is a part.

We must start with a working definition of 'community' and then review the critical factors involved in determining a community's health status. With these, we can describe the behaviours that would be required of providers, and how the role of payers could change to encourage providers to act as an instrument for the community's health. Finally the roles of individual patients and of government in facilitating such a new orientation will be discussed.

THE COMMUNITY AND THE COMMUNITY'S HEALTH

There is an extensive, sometimes contradictory and always controversial literature defining 'the community' in various contexts (1,2). My working definition of 'community' is a defined population for which a provider assumes responsibility. The payer/purchaser provides incentives for the provider to achieve the goal of this new relationship – improvement in community health status.

What are the critical influences on a community's health status? The effectiveness of the health care delivery system is clearly only one factor and probably not the most important. I have listed the parameters proposed for measuring the health of a city, which were developed as part of the World Health Organisation's (WHO) Healthy Cities project. The project seeks to develop comprehensive strategies to address the array of factors involved in urban health status.

PARAMETERS TO MEASURE THE HEALTH OF A CITY

1. Demography: the balance of economic, ethnic, socio-economic status and educational levels among the population of a community.

2. Quality of the physical environment: includes the presence of pollution, the quality of the infrastructure especially energy, water, sewage disposal, housing, communication systems and transportation.

3. State of the local economy: includes employment/unemployment levels.

4. Quality of the social environment: includes levels of psycho-social stress, the quality of social support services and the strength and nature of local culture(s).

5. Personal safety.

6. Aesthetics of the environment and the quality of life.

---

(1) Bates, E. Health Systems and Public Scrutiny. Croom Helm 1983.
(2) Health Care Systems in Transition – The Search for Efficiency'. OECD Social Policy Studies No. 7 1990.

7. Appropriate education.

8. Extent of community participation, structures of government.

9. New health promotion indicators: refers to the focus on personal behaviour change as a factor in health status: levels of participation in physical exercise, dietary habits, alcohol and tobacco use may indicate the success of health promotion and disease prevention efforts.

10. Quality of health services.

11. Traditional health indicators (mortality and morbidity).

12. Equity: refers to the citizen's opportunity for and access to the full array of these human services and community resources.

There is significant research indicating that factors such as housing, jobs and education probably have more significant long term effects on health status than more traditionally emphasised parameters such as healthy behaviours and health services; but all are important.(3)

The kind of 'intersectoral collaboration' required to influence the full array of variables affecting the community's health can only come from governmental efforts to bring a 'health orientation' to the work of its various administrative divisions of labour, education, housing, environment, health and social services. The municipal level of government is the operating unit of the Healthy Cities project. In the US, the Federal government is the agent in the WHO 'Health For All 2000' programme. Our focus on the changes needed in the health care delivery system to improve the community's health requires us to identify the proper level of authority – governmental or administrative – at which we can influence this system on behalf of a defined community.

In the UK, the National Health Service District Health Authority (DHA) is now explicitly defined as purchaser of care on behalf of the individuals living in that district. The role includes securing overall improvements in the health status of this geographically defined population. The parallel payer/purchaser unit relating to a geographically defined population in the United States system would be the State, since the organisation, regulation and financing framework of the US health care delivery system tends to vary by State. Within each of these larger units are institutional and

---

(3) **Research Unit in Health and Behavioural Change Edinburgh: 'Changing the Public Health'. John Wesley, 1989.**

individual providers relating to sub-populations in smaller communities that will logically be the operational focus of change efforts. But what do we want these providers to do?

PROVIDER BEHAVIOURS

The following diagram identifies types of interventions needed to promote the community's health (horizontal axis); the potential targets of the intervention – the individual, the community or the institution (vertical axis); and the impact of these interventions on the third dimension of this diagram, the continuum from illness to health. Institutional (and, to a lesser degree, individual) providers are in a position to act at each of these levels, if they are aware of that potential and provided with the proper incentives – financial, regulatory, or political – to do so.

Starting in the lower left corner, clinical medical care is focused on identification, treatment and rehabilitation of acute and chronic illness. The target population is the individual patient who seeks medical attention.

Kerr White (4) followed one thousand individuals over the course of a year and found that from this thousand 750 experienced some health complaint of which 250 sought medical attention; 33 of these were admitted to a community hospital and one to a teaching hospital. Applying these findings to our evaluation of efforts to promote the community's health, we realise that the hospital, clearly the focal point of the traditional delivery system, is needed by less than 15 per cent of individuals who enter the formal health care system. Most are treated in an ambulatory care or primary care setting.

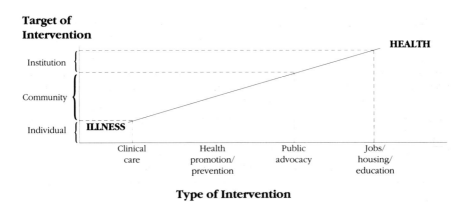

Target of Intervention

Institution

Community

Individual

ILLNESS

HEALTH

Clinical care · Health promotion/ prevention · Public advocacy · Jobs/ housing/ education

Type of Intervention

(4) White, Kerr and Greenburg. 'The Ecology of Health' NEJM 1963.

There is very little argument that this area, either directly or through affiliated programmes, is a prime responsibility of provider institutions – large and small. Most of the current debate in the US focuses on how (not whether) to enhance the provider role in the areas of primary care and prevention for the individual patient. A constraint here is the inadequate financing of primary care and virtual absence of financing of preventive services for the individual.

Moving out along the continuum from illness towards health, we enter the realm of interventions targeted at the community, that is, expanding beyond the individual seeking care towards these individuals who do not necessarily come to medical attention. Community health promotion (via health education) and disease prevention (immunisation drives, cancer screening) through the delivery system are, again, a less controversial area for 'the provider', though they are less well developed, primarily due to the lack of institutional interest and of funding.

Asking providers to use their institutional resources and influence to address other factors affecting community health status – environment, jobs, education – is, however, entering new and untested territory.

When confronted about their failures to address the health problems of 'the community', US provider institutions often reply that organised medicine (or medical education in the case of teaching hospitals) cannot take on the problems of the health care delivery system, especially a reimbursement system that neither provides universal health insurance coverage nor rewards primary care specialties. Further they argue, not inappropriately, that the poor health status of certain groups of the population, especially minorities and the poor, are complex and multifactorial involving issues of economics, housing, jobs; therefore, society (that is the government) must be held responsible.

Shroeder (5) argues in a recent article in JAMA that academic medical centres hold a public trust. Of 127 medical schools in the United States, 77 (61 per cent) are public. In addition, public subsidies for patient care (Medicaid, Medicare), research (NIH) and tax benefits, grants and contracts provide more than 50 per cent of the resources of all academic medical centres in the United States. He exhorts academic medical centres to see their central mission as the improvement in the health of a defined population and cites as barriers to change:
- faculty resistance to changing traditional patterns;
- difficulties in changing clinical educational models;
- the intractability of many of the social problems underlying inadequate health status;
- the multifactorial nature of health.

---

(5) Schroeder, S.A., Zones, J.S. and Showstack, J.A. 'Academic Medicine as a Public Trust'. JAMA 1989:262:803-12.

Another impediment to more sophisticated community health activities in the US has been the traditional separation of the public health function – concerning itself with the health of population groups (denominator) – from the clinical medical providers – focusing on the individual (numerator). In the US, the public health system has been greatly neglected over the last decade as federal support has been withdrawn for the traditional public health functions and states have made hard choices over tight health and human service budgets. With the exception of so called categorical funding for AIDS and maternal child services, little new money has been injected into this system in recent years. Most State departments of public health perform their minimum legal requirements under the State health code, but few have the resources or the linkage to the health care delivery system to serve as an effective bridge to influence the clinical delivery system in the direction of a concern with the health status of the community.

Drawing on these elements, one could make a list of the kind of 'provider behaviours' that would need to be encouraged to shift a 'patient' oriented health care delivery system toward a greater role as an instrument for improved community health. The provider should:

1. Identify a defined population (community) for which the provider assumes responsibility.

2. Develop links to that community through individuals and organisations.

3. Begin to bring the volume and types of services it delivers into line with the health needs of its defined population and assure their appropriateness and cost effectiveness.

4. Develop effective primary care systems in the community, that can link the patients to the level and intensity of resources needed at the appropriate stage of health and illness.

5. Identify health problems in the defined community susceptible to effective preventive/health promotion/and health advocacy interventions; work with the community to define priorities; and mount a campaign for community intervention as well as patient intervention in a 'design – implement – evaluate – modify and add' programme cycle.

6. Develop institutional programmes focusing on the health status of the institutional work force, including health benefits.

7. Develop a role as institutional advocate in the community to increase

70

the healthy choices available to the population in schools, work places and commercial establishments in identified problem areas.

8. Develop a role using institutional economic leverage within the community for 'health related' changes:
    ● jobs for residents in the community
    ● channelling purchasing and contracting power to community institutions
    ● housing development via capital leverage
    ● education programmes for health careers and health education.

Some hospitals in the US are already involved in many of these activities, often as part of marketing strategies or because they are the sole community provider. The Kellogg Foundation has recently initiated the development of a voluntary accreditation programme for hospitals to meet certain 'Community Benefit Standards'. Their eventual hope is to influence payers to reward such behaviour by selective contracting and/or premium rates.

Prepaid practice organisations (HMOs, PPOs, IPAs), providing the full range of health services to enrolled beneficiaries, have some incentives to develop at least the first four kinds of programmes listed above. However, as competition increased, these 'institutional' providers find it more and more difficult to initiate and/or sustain real community oriented health programmes without additional financial support aimed at achieving these ends.

The primary care provider (individual practitioner or small group), will find virtually none of the community oriented activities reimbursable and will be unlikely to take on such a role. There is an interest in the US in the potential of Community Oriented Primary Care (COPC) shifting a primary care practice towards a community health focus. The major obstacles are practitioner education and financing.

Thus, if real change is to be initiated and sustained over the period of time necessary to get the health care delivery system to 'do business differently', in the interest of the community, the provider cannot do it alone. The payer will have to behave differently.

NEW PAYER BEHAVIOURS

The biggest problem facing US providers who wish to be more community orientated is the lack of a basic set of health insurance benefits for all citizens. Clearly, the structuring of such a benefit package to include primary care, prevention and health promotion services to individuals would be an enormous boost to the kind or provider change we are

71

discussing at the service delivery level. Since such a uniform action on health care financing at the federal level is unlikely, given the US penchant for pluralism and heterogeneity, the most realistic focus for any such payment reform is likely to be at the State level.

If a State chose to develop an all payer system under which all private insurers, Blue Cross/Blue Shield, Medicaid and (via a federal waiver) Medicare would be subject to the same rules, a basic benefits package could be developed and provided for all beneficiaries at an identified rate. The uninsured might be covered by a restructuring of a bad debt and charity care pool as in New York State, by a tax on all payers or by State subsidised small-employer requirements.

Financial incentives could be structured to provide 'rate plus' reimbursement for those providers which implement and maintain a series of community oriented activities such as those listed above. The State could define its priorities through regulations or a special 'experimental' financing initiative and could structure provider incentives to reward these behaviours. As noted, the most important provider behaviour would be: identifying a population for which it assumes responsibility; developing links to that community; working with the community to define health problems for action; developing effective primary care systems, and balancing the services provided with community need. Because of the pluralism of the US system, mechanisms would be needed to encourage consortium development among providers at all levels within a defined area. Plans could be submitted to the State to define the provider consortium, the community collaborators and the community oriented health improvement plan. State approval of the provider's plan would initiate enhanced rates. The public health services of the State Department of Health could be linked to the delivery side at the State and local level to assist in population health status data collection and analysis; technical assistance for intervention design; and evaluation and monitoring of the community health plan effectiveness over time.

The State role as regulator, as well as rate setter, would also be critical to the success of such an effort, since identification of potential opportunities for health care delivery systems savings to invest in such a strategy would require regulatory intervention. Some options could include: mandatory assignment of those making extensive use of publicly financed (Medicaid) into a managed care plan; a State administered one payer system could result in decreased administrative overhead for providers and insurers; 'sin taxes' could be raised on alcohol and tobacco targetted to financing of the health care system or this particular community health initiative; the State could best assume an aggressive role in eliminating excess capacity and regulate technology acquisition; in the process of consortium development the State could convene expert panels to address appropriateness of certain high cost procedures to guide reimbursement decisions. While hospital reimbursement systems are easier to structure, primary care providers who implement COPC or other community health oriented initiatives could similarly receive enhanced rates or, more easily, be eligible for categorical funding to support these community health programmes.

PATIENT BEHAVIOURS

The final actor in the payer-provider-patient triad – the patient – must also change his/her behaviour to begin to act as part of a community of interest. This will be much more difficult in the US than in the UK. In the latter, there is a stronger sense of the obligations of 'the State' to provide equity in access to basic human services on the understanding that though this may mean not having everything, at least everyone has access to the same basic benefits. The US seems to have a natural value conflict between equity and individuality. The health care financing system continues to guarantee individuals the right to consume as much care as they can afford. Certain citizens are denied access, except in situations of extreme need as a consequence. Recent government action to look at 'medical appropriateness' as a criterion for reimbursement and initiatives by states like Oregon in the public 'rationing' of care may signal a change in this overriding cultural value.

The barriers to effective patient/community involvement in health care decision-making at all levels must also be addressed. They are varied and include: apathy, lack of technical knowledge, lack of effective structures, and imbalance in power relationships, among others.

In the US, there is very little community involvement at the payer/purchaser (or policy) level in the health care system, since the virtual abolition of the National Health Planning Acts of the 1970s. These provided for (perhaps overly) elaborate structures of graded public representation from the local community level to the State level via the Health Systems Agencies (HSAs). These bodies were given a required consultative role (although arguably with little real authority) in health service planning and resource investment decisions for their geographic area. Final recommendations were forwarded to the state governor for action through a State Hospital Review and Planning Council (SHRPC). In addition, each State had a State Health Co-ordinating Committee (SHCC) charged with the development of a State Health Plan drawing on the recommendations of the local HSAs. With a legally required 51 per cent 'consumer' representation, but with little uniform guidance on the definition of a consumer, these bodies often got bogged down in political power struggles. The State government's willingness to enforce the HSA recommendations on providers was also variable.

From this experience, State governments would be in a position to develop more effective structures to reintroduce community involvement at the policy level of the payer/purchaser. This kind of structure would be a logical part of a comprehensive community-oriented health initiative.

In the US, there tend to be more structures for institutionally based 'community input', such as boards of trustees of voluntary and public hospitals and community advisory boards of community health centres; some would question the 'representativeness' of these structures. If an institutional provider took on a broader role as an instrument for the community's health, it would be logical to review the appropriateness of its existing community involvement, to assure its ability to meet the goal of real community collaboration.

The payer must change behaviour to create incentives, but this can only happen if there is a more general reorientation of culture in the health care delivery system among policy makers, providers and patients. This culture must shift from one dominated by the individual's medical needs to one with a more expanded focus on the health of the community. Such a transformation will also require considerable information about what this means, why it's important and how to achieve it. The first step is a realisation of the increased effectiveness of a community oriented health care delivery system as a part of a comprehensive effort to promote better community health status. The authority for a co-ordinated effort of education and implementation across all sectors logically rests with government, but the leadership for change could well come from those in the health care sector.

Conclusion
(Editor)

These varying papers demonstrate the difficulty in practice of changing focus – and how crucial it is to do so. Provider dominance must change if health goals are to be met. Crafting a different 'game' requires great skill and tenacity and a willingness of all 'players' to move and be flexible. We now move on to this theme in more detail.

THE 'F' PLAN PART II: KEEPING FAST AND FLEXIBLE

Health care systems, especially those without market forces or business stimuli, have not been noted for speed of reaction. This has been, sometimes, because of their location in the public sector where an appropriate response to a problem might be a Royal Commission or a government statement. It can also be sheer complexity. Someone once remarked that, were the planet to be destroyed except for a large district general or teaching hospital, the whole world could be recreated from it. Whatever the reason, the idea of fast and flexible responses to both problems and opportunities has been viewed with puzzlement. Equally, the idea that speed is both possible and desirable is still something that surprises some senior managers and professionals. I often ask the question, while acting as a consultant – 'What is stopping you doing it now?'. Often the truthful answer is, 'very little'.

The preceding chapter has argued the case for focus and vision. If the organisation is not capable of some kind of speed in its response, such an effort may come to nothing. It is a wearying thing to say, but true, that if you stand still and think too long you may need to think again – the world has a habit of moving on. Getting rid of slow bureaucratic response does more than speed things up. More importantly, it ensures frequent and appropriate interaction between organisations and their environment which can make best use of creative opportunities and minimise the impact of real problems. Paralysis and slowness can have devastating consequences and may lie at the root of wars, famines and pestilences – not to mention foreign exchange difficulties. Frustration with the slowness of bureaucracies and the unresponsiveness of political systems to change can produce many results! Dictatorship – 'at least they got the trains to run on time' – one-party rule to avoid complex value issues – totalitarianism – the management of change by central dictat – all have been tried and found wanting. The challenge is to find a new way which respects different interests in a pluralistic world, which allows power struggles to be open, honest and accessible, which permits rules and precedents to have their place and yet can move.

A similar dissatisfaction is evident in the movement away from public bureaucracies in Western liberal democracies and the assertion of liberal and market principles – to the point where many writers assert an end to fundamental ideological and philosophical debate (1).

The previous chapter has raised the issue of values as a legitimate barrier to action. This section will consider other blocks and how to overcome them. A key point, made frequently during the conference concerning the United States, highlighted this aspect. The US is designed to say 'no' and make change hard – thus all the consensus about the inevitability of change in the health care system may fall on stony ground.

Most of the interesting and challenging issues in organisations fall outside established departments and job descriptions. Dramatic changes of the 1980s came when entire populations walked round and through their existing organisations and knocked them down – in Prague and Berlin and Bucharest. Mrs Thatcher in the UK cried 'off with their heads' quite frequently, and off they came.

The obligation to move around in a constructive 'focused' fashion falls to politicians, managers and professionals. Many conference papers discussed these dances at federal, state, organisational and micro level. Some were 'failures', in the sense that there appeared to be no-one better off at the end, and/or some worse off. Others were 'winners', where fast and flexible responses allowed one or more players to obtain real gain.

Within organisations, creative energy can be used to 'buck the system', play games, and avoid responsibility, or it can be harnessed. We still don't really know how to do this consistently, but some truths are beginning to emerge.

The role of individuals and the quality of 'management', as well as of 'managers', is clearly important. These disparate examples are united by the need for key players or thinkers to turn problems into opportunities – potential for conflict into potential for agreement – and build in success (however small), rather than deliberate endlessly over failure. The failures can be seen as involving players in a different game – slow, inflexible – bureaucratic, not focused. The comparisons are interesting.

The United Kingdom on the move

(Editor)

The next paper takes, as a case study, the 1990-1991 changes in the British National Health Service. Throughout the conference the spectre of NHS reform lurked, even for non-British delegates. A national, cost effective and

---

(1) Fukuyama, F. The End of Ideology. The National Interest, No 16 1989.

comprehensive system was on the move. The destination and purpose of the journey were unclear and this became a constant reference point and case history – especially as it coincided with the USA. beginning to stagger uncertainly in what appears to be an opposing direction. In place of a clear 'focus', it is interesting to consider the various moves or changes and what is driving them, in order to see where the whole 'system' may be leading. As already noted, notions of a purchaser/provider split, or 'market forces' are meaningless until and unless behaviour of individuals and organisations changes.

Christine Hancock looks at the impetus for change within the NHS and then considers the various responses that will be necessary from the key actors. Unlike Jo Boufford's earlier paper, with a more philosophical focus, this paper actually tells us that it is task-focused – an attempt to offer a framework for overcoming barriers to successful change.

A FRAMEWORK FOR MOVEMENT

CHRISTINE HANCOCK (UNITED KINGDOM)

INTRODUCTION

The United Kingdom experience of managing and delivering health care and the domestic political context and agenda for change provides the focus for my paper. However, it also draws, to a limited extent, on parallel developments in the United States where these appear (a) to provide the ideological or theoretical underpinning for UK governmental initiatives; (b) to suggest possible pitfalls or models for further developments within the UK; or (c) to illuminate cultural differences which may affect the successful transfer of US models to the UK context.

The paper is task-focused: it attempts to offer a framework for overcoming barriers to successful change which can be tested, validated or revised against the actual experience of managers and professionals.

THE IMPETUS FOR CHANGE

The driving force behind the British Government's desire to reform the structure of health and social care provision is concern and frustration over certain key deficiencies in the delivery of care. These include:

● escalating costs, and a perception that resources are deployed more effectively in some areas than others;

● intractably long waiting lists for elective surgery in many parts of the UK;

● patchy and inappropriate services for certain 'priority' patient groups, in particular people with a mental illness, mental handicap, disabilities or chronic illnesses and for elderly people;

● inflexibility and unresponsiveness to the consumer.

Each of these concerns is legitimate. However, there are other equally compelling challenges facing health and social care services which have not been adequately acknowledged and are not fully addressed by the strategies adopted by Government. These are:

78

- the pressures of demography;

- providing quality care for an ageing population in the context of a shortage of skilled labour;

- the impact of new diseases (such as AIDS);

- the relationship between paid and unpaid carers; and

- rising consumer expectations.

THE VEHICLE FOR CHANGE

The UK Government has chosen the market model as its vehicle for change. An element of managed competition is being introduced into the National Health Service, and to a lesser extent into the structures for delivering social care in the community. Responsibility for funding or purchasing services has been separated from responsibility for delivering or providing care. The relationship between purchasers and providers is to be governed by competitive contracts as a spur to greater responsiveness to service users.

The culture shock induced by these changes should not be underestimated, particularly as the complex organisational changes necessary to achieve them are being imposed on a reluctant service at breakneck speed. The reliance on the market model is essentially ideological. It is based on no proven experience that a market culture can be effective in health care but is consistent with Conservative philosophies of importing business principles into the public sector and of 'getting close to the customer'. There is however, as yet, no real evidence that the market can effect the improvements in health care delivery which are hoped from it, although claims have been made about the efficacy of established NHS Trusts since 1991.

This gap is most starkly apparent in the arena of consumer choice. Real consumer choice depends, crucially, on access to adequate information about services upon which to make a rational decision, on a range of alternatives from which to choose and on the capacity to enforce the choice made. Data on cost, quality and effectiveness are vital ingredients of the information package.

Yet the know-how to establish effective measures in these areas and about outcomes resides almost exclusively with the providers of services. Purchasers may find difficulty in gaining access to disinterested advice on which to make their purchasing decisions and lack experience in the manipulation of contracts. In principle, the separation of funding from provision could provide purchasing agencies with a powerful incentive to exert positive and progressive leverage over providers to secure a range of services tailored to the needs of their resident populations, rather than to the preferences of the professionals. In practice, the emergence of cost-effective, care-effective provision is likely to be entirely fortuitous.

> *There is no market to control the managers. If the managers of a supermarket chain fail to be sensitive to consumer needs, the market will punish him or her. If the Health Authority fails to be sensitive to consumer needs, there is no such mechanism.* (1)

The structures of accountability are defective in two respects: given the likelihood of continuing resource constraints, health authority managers, that is, purchasers, are likely to perceive their accountability primarily upwards to regional and national level and to focus on meeting budget targets and constraining expenditure. The accountability 'downwards' or 'outwards' to service users is entirely absent.

In addition, therefore, to the barriers to choice which derive from an absence of meaningful information, users' dependence on professional expertise and their lack of involvement in the planning of service provision, there is the overarching constraint that users of the service cannot opt out of the market. They have no ability to purchase services directly and their participation in medical treatment is not an optional consumer luxury. In the context of 'market' language, it is worth remembering that.

> *Health consumers (and this includes both the 'buyers' and the 'recipients' of care): (1) do not enter the acute care 'market' at will; (2) do not leave this 'market' at will; (3) are constrained by the depth and breadth of information provided to/for them, by the lack of outcome measures, by often critical time factors, and by the services available to them locally.* (2)

Managers who are enthusiastic exponents of the new structures, argue that the recognition that each patient effectively carries a price tag with them will strengthen consumer power.

---

(1) Klein, R. 'Looking After Consumers in the NHS'. British Medical Journal, 300, 26 May 1990, 1351-1352.
(2) Curtin, L. 'Economic Competition: Has the 'solution' become the problem?'. Nursing Management, 20(5), May 7-8 1989.

When patients realise that they represent a source of money, they themselves will try to exert an influence on which particular units they go to. And the sort of thing influencing patient choice is the quality aspect of the service. There will be real pressure on providers to demonstrate the quality that they provide. (3)

This argument is dangerously over-optimistic, if not recklessly naive in its assessment of the capacity of vulnerable people to make choices and take control over their care. It also assumes that it is acceptable for better units to thrive and for the less efficient to go to the wall. For some patients, the market spur on a unit to become more effective may come too late.

THE LANGUAGE OF CHANGE

There is little doubt that the reforms of the NHS have been greeted with a mixture of anxiety and hostility by the general public and health care professionals alike. Part of that hostility stems from the language used to promote change. The espousal of business principles and market ideologies is probably the defining characteristic of the past decade of Government. Its impact has been felt in every sphere of public and social policy and has effected a fundamental shift in the infrastructures which underpin public life in the United Kingdom. Nevertheless, public opinion and social attitudes have not undergone a matching transformation. A comprehensive opinion poll, 'Britain under the MORIscope', July 1990 demonstrated that support for collective solutions and a reliance on public provision, however paternalistic, is still deeply rooted. (4)

Individually, whether as parents, teachers, consumers of public services or workers within those services, almost every citizen has felt the impact of the market approach, and the experience has not always been positive. Each policy initiative has been undermined by a failure to pump-prime the changes with additional resources or, worse still, has been accompanied by a cost-cutting exercise which has fatally undermined public and professional acceptance of change.

The general public may not have a sophisticated understanding of the structures of health care delivery and is probably merely perplexed by the theoretical language of purchasers and providers. It is, however, shrewd enough to concur with the view that, 'the fundamental difficulty is that the

---

(3) Jackson, C. **Birmingham Post, 12 July 1990.**
(4) Jacobs, E. and Worcester, R. **'We British: Britain under the MORIscope' 1990.**

Government has this ideological notion that you can improve quality dramatically without improving resources'. (5)

These perceptions are shared even more acutely by the nurses, doctors and other health care workers in the service, who are often alienated by the language, concept and application of the market.

It is important to recall that for most health care professionals and public sector managers, the prospect of individual reward for performance has never been the motivating factor influencing their choice of a career. The ethos of public service may not be currently fashionable, but is more likely to yield the crusading zeal without which efforts to redirect the emphasis of medical and nursing services away from the curative model and towards health promotion, are unlikely to be successful.

The flip side of the current Government's espousal of the entrepreneurial culture is a climate in which many dedicated and experienced staff feel that their value systems are no longer regarded as valid and that their working methods are caricatured as the last bastion of Fabian paternalism. That feeling of resentful inadequacy is reinforced by the poor educational and managerial base characteristic of public services in this country. The United Kingdom's poor record in the provision of in-service and continuing education threatens to undermine the ability of the NHS to deliver the planned reforms.

In the context of nursing, there is also a recent and powerful folk memory of the traumatic introduction of general management. While it would be fair to acknowledge that the response of senior nurses to the challenge of general management was unimaginative and defensive, it remains the case that a large cohort of experienced and well-regarded senior nurses was swept aside into retirement with the advent of general management. Nursing has struggled ever since to establish a proper niche within the NHS structure.

Right across the NHS, existing management teams were broken up, individual staff lacked the educational base which would have helped them to respond flexibly and the resulting demoralisation has continuing adverse effects even today. It is a major challenge for the NHS Management Executive to create a climate where this unhappy cycle of insecurity and alienation is avoided.

THE NEW POWER BROKERS

Within the semi-closed world of the health service, the issue of power dominates the agenda. It is widely assumed that providers, and in particular

---

(5) Taylor, M. Birmingham Post, 12 July 1990.

the self-governing trusts and budget holding GP practices, will emerge as the new power brokers. Considerable effort is being directed towards an analysis of how the balance of power might be tilted in favour of purchasing agencies.

The underlying assumption appears to be that there is an infinite demand for health services, but finite resources to meet them. Without adequate controlling mechanisms, the argument runs, the combination of professional expertise and financial semi-autonomy will allow providers of services to exert almost total control over the scope, quality and pattern of health care delivery.

Philip Hunt, director of the National Association of Health Authorities, argued in a lecture to the Royal Institute of Public Administration, that health authorities, far from being the key players in the new structures, could find themselves on 'a slippery and downhill road, heading towards eventual redundancy'. (6) His solution involves ensuring that health authority purchasing decisions are based on a comprehensive and imaginative assessment of the health needs of the resident population.

Needs assessment, rather than demand management, offers a positive route forward. The notion of infinite demand for NHS services is a dangerous myth which has undermined the efforts for all organisations attempting to lobby for better resourcing. It has arisen in the context of decades of actual rising demand, but in the absence of a coherent health strategy – based on known demographic factors, epidemiological data and a positive commitment to the promotion of health rather than the treatment of sickness. It also ignores the fact that most people, given the right information, will use services responsibly.

Potentially, the emphasis on meeting the needs of a defined resident population, should provide a powerful incentive towards the provision of appropriate services and should give purchasers considerable financial leverage which they may choose to exert progressively. Provider units will depend on their ability to attract contracts. Primary health care and public health objectives should emerge more powerfully. Primary prevention, and improved outcomes of health status, reduced incidence of disease, lower mortality and morbidity from common conditions, earlier detection and treatment, lower readmission rates and better rehabilitation services should all move higher up the health care agenda. Quality and equity of services are now also making a welcome, if belated, entrance into the vocabulary of NHS managers. If purchasers' contracting decisions are to be influenced by quality criteria, as well as cost and volume, they will be specifying not just what and how much will be provided, but also how – the process as

---

(6) **Hunt, P. Lecture to the Royal Institute of Public Administration 17 July 1990 – unpublished.**

well as the structure. They may choose to use this process lever in a wide variety of contexts, to ensure, for example, that providers manage against discrimination both in the provision of services to a racially diverse resident population but also in their employment practices. However, this optimistic scenario will not automatically be fulfilled. The experience of the United States is instructive, if not conclusive.

THE AMERICAN EXPERIENCE

In a Shattuck lecture, Paul M Ellwood Jr, MD, reveals that measures parallel to those being introduced in the United Kingdom were set in train in the USA as early as 1969, in response to a presidential declaration that the nation faced a health care crisis.

> *Costs were surging. Patients were beginning to challenge the authority of doctors and doubts were being raised about the efficacy of some medical procedures. The response to the crisis was a bold federal policy aimed at restructuring the organisation and incentives of the entire American health care enterprise. The policy to restructure provoked a trend, then a mass movement toward a health care system influenced by market forces, incentive-based payment arrangements, and aggregations of providers.* (7)

By any objective criteria, the policy cannot be described as successful. Health costs in the United States have continued to escalate, yet as many as 35 million people have no or little health cover at all. Corporate America faces a 25 per cent increase in health costs each year for employee insurance; and socialised medicine, despite its traditional association with rationing, is beginning to enjoy a respectable following. As A. Eugene Le Blanc, executive director of Policy Development for the Ontario Ministry of Health argues, 'The fact that some Americans have access to distinguished medical services while millions have none, seems like rationing to me. I have never understood why Americans stand for it'. (8)

For corporate America even to consider the possibility of opting for a national system of health insurance is a dramatic testimony to the inadequacy of the market concept.

Of course, the picture is not uniform. For some considerable time, providers – both in the sense of units and in the sense of individual

---

(7) Ellwood, P.M. 'Outcomes Management: the Technology of Patient Experience' New England Journal of Medicine, 318, 9 June 1988, 1549-1556.
(8) Le Blanc, A.E. Washington Post, 18 December 1989.

physicians – continued to set the health care agenda and proved adept at manipulating control mechanisms, such as diagnostic related groups and item-for-service payments. Purchasers have learnt from the experience and are beginning to exert much greater leverage through systems of remuneration which assess quality and effectiveness of care, health outcomes as well as inputs.

The challenge for the United Kingdom is to bypass or overleap the US learning process and parachute into the contract process at a much more sophisticated and health-progressive stage.

> *The prospects for so doing are not bright. The United Kingdom risks importing the negative features of the US market in health care, without its matching and highly developed system of accreditation and regulation. The House of Commons Social Services Select Committee warned in August 1989 that the scope for gaming, price-fixing and for the emergence of anti-competitive cartels, is worryingly great. (9)*

Within the US experience, different strands can be observed. Some purchasers, like California Blue Cross, are successfully constructing contract mechanisms which place an incentive, even an obligation, on providers to embrace health promotion and to keep their citizens healthy. In other areas traditional medical models dominate so that a providers' unit like John Hopkins in Baltimore offers a beacon of clinical excellence in complete isolation from a deprived ghetto hinterland.

Any purchaser or provider organisation will be composed of a coalition of interests. It seems, however, to be a matter of chance whether the dominant coalition is progressive or regressive. Again, the challenge for the United Kingdom must be to tease out those factors which favour the emergence of the primary health care, progressive approach.

A FRAMEWORK FOR PROGRESS: PATIENT POWER

The debate around overcoming provider dominance has, to date, focused largely on the search for mechanisms which will strengthen the purchaser's position. That search is probably misplaced.

It would be more relevant to seek to enhance the ability of the third

---

(9) House of Commons Social Services. 'Eighth report session 1988-1989: Resourcing the National Health Service: the Government's plans for the future of the National Health Service, together with the proceedings of the Committee'. London. HMSO 1989.

force – patients – to exercise control and choice over health care provision. The White Papers which provided the ideological underpinning for the National Health Service reforms are long on the rhetoric of consumer choice but the legislation in fact gives consumers no greater power in decision-making within the structure. Indeed, it could be argued that the greater emphasis on managerial accountability is incompatible with a greater role for consumers in the planning of services.

In order to effect a shift in the balance of power towards the consumer, it will be necessary to help them to raise expectations, to challenge the judgements and decisions of clinical staff and to demand the courtesy and respect which is their due and without which they cannot feel secure enough to demand better care.

The still largely unassailable citadel of clinical freedom will have to be scaled, doctors and nurses will have to surrender some of their independence and patients will need to become less passive.

It is a formidable challenge, but not insuperable. In the UK context, it has simply not been attempted before. Structures which inform and empower patients will be needed in all three power bases: among purchasers, providers and patients themselves.

THE CHALLENGE FOR PURCHASERS

Credible structures of accountability will need to be created which allow users and user groups an input to the planning and monitoring of services. Comprehensive information, in user-friendly language and in minority languages, must be provided about local services and local plans. Purchasers must be willing to incorporate user performance into their contract specifications and to terminate contracts with inflexible providers.

THE CHALLENGE FOR PROVIDERS

Self-regulation does not empower the user. An independent inspection mechanism, with user involvement, has been resisted by Government, but the arguments in favour of it will continue to gather strength. The UK has not adopted the US accreditation model, relying instead on arms length inspection arrangements for community care and an as yet embryonic Clinical Standards Advisory Group for the NHS setting.

Within provider organisations, there will need to be a quiet revolution. Nurses, midwives, health visitors, physiotherapists and others will need to assert their autonomy and challenge the traditional dominance of the medical establishment. This, in itself, would strengthen consumer choice by providing patients with a range of practitioners to whom they could have direct access.

These groups are also better placed, because their professional ethos is not curative and disease focused, to embrace health promotion in a meaningful way. The health care team will need to learn to share power with the consumer. Only then can patients take control of their care.

An individual without information cannot take responsibility; an individual who is given information cannot help but take responsibility. (10)

The professional organisations which represent individual providers will need to forge new links with the organised representatives of patients, offering the expertise upon which effective monitoring and advocacy services can be built.

When drawing up tenders for contracts, providers must be responsive to the declared wishes of consumers and to seek their involvement in standard setting. Patient-centred quality assurance tools which value the patient's perception of the effectiveness of their care must be developed.

Willing participation in user liaison groups and effective complaints mechanisms must be evolved.

THE CHALLENGE TO PATIENTS

The challenge to patients lies in balancing an assertion of individual rights with an acceptance of personal responsibility.

Although the NHS has a long way to go before it meets the quite legitimate expectations of quality of personal service which would be considered routine in the United States, the flip-side of assertive consumerism – excessive recourse to litigation and excessive investigations and treatment – must be avoided. The best mechanism for avoiding that route lies in structures for patient participation and control which are disinterested and have a collective focus.

Major changes in clinical practice have been achieved in the United Kingdom by the combined influence of powerful pressure groups and advocacy in the field of mental illness, mental handicap, childbirth and childcare. A new alliance of consumer and provider groups is now needed for mutual strength and support in a period of rapid change and continuing resource constraint. Only thus can the dimension of quality

---

(10) Carlton, J. Riv Pyramidernal! In. Peters, T. 'Thriving on Chaos'. Pan London 1989.

assume its rightful central role in the planning, delivery and perception of care.

A THREE-WAY PARTNERSHIP FOR THE FUTURE

The introduction of competitive clinical contracts remains controversial and their efficacy unproven. However, it seems likely that it is the competitive element, rather than the contract mechanism, which will pose problems for the UK service. If purchasers and providers respond imaginatively to the contract culture, a powerful quality assurance tool will emerge. However, to be fully effective, a three-way contract which also confers rights and responsibilities on the patient is needed. The concept is being mooted within the context of community care. It could prove to be the lever which brings the uncertain and shifting power blocks within health care into a harmonious equilibrium.

Summary
(Editor)

The force majeure *of a dogmatic government could not be resisted even by powerful groups. The essential question, therefore, is how far key groups can move fast and flexibly enough to hang onto key values and produce a good outcome, as they see it. Lack of response would have made the situation worse.*

Can the private sector move faster?
(Editor)

It is often assumed, even if not articulated, that the private sector in the formerly British countries – with its invisible hand, 'free market', and the entry and exit of capital – is, by definition, much more responsive than the public sector. It can certainly be suggested that it has more chance to be so, when the need for public accountability, deliberations of national resource allocation and rationing are removed and relatively simple transactions are all that is required. However, the private sector is bedevilled with failures resulting in bankruptcy and the collapse of corporations – it is clearly not immune from pressures of its own.

A major change in publicly funded systems, particularly in the United Kingdom and increasingly in Sweden, was the introduction of business principles and an internal market to improve the management of health care. The following paper, written by a manager with public and private sector experience draws some specific lessons from his experience as a contribution to this area.

Sandy Bradbrook, in anticipation of the NHS reforms which have now been more fully implemented, draws some parallels between his experience in the business world and the new roles emerging in the NHS. While some restructuring has taken place in parallel with the changing roles it is essential that flexibility is a key word.

CAN THE PRIVATE SECTOR PROVIDE A MODEL FOR FASTER MOVEMENT?

DR J SANDY BRADBROOK (UNITED KINGDOM)

This paper is intended to provide points of issue that have general applicability. They are derived from a combination of my fifteen years in senior management in manufacturing industries, my last seven years as a district general manager in the NHS in the UK, and from my expectations as to the future NHS following the implementation of the 1990 Act.

CHANGING ROLES AND DEMAND

THE DISTRICT HEALTH AUTHORITY (DHA) AS 'PAYER'

The DHA receives funds for its resident population from the Government (via the Region) and is charged with obtaining the best packages of care to meet the 'health needs' of the resident population.

The essential roles of the DHA equivalent to a commercial organisation are:

i)   market research;

ii) purchasing;

iii) monitoring performance;

iv) communicating performance to its shareholders.

A well-known public company which operates world-wide in this fashion is 'Air-Wick'. Its success can be very simply measured in terms of profitability, growth and liquidity. It does not ultimately matter what products it markets and variations in revenue are substantially controllable by the Company. Its suppliers are required to produce a product to a quality, price and delivery programme, and the product performance is clear in terms of outcome.

The DHAs (or their equivalent purchasing agents in other health care systems) are characterised currently by having:

v)   a fixed revenue, with possibly a declining purchasing power;

vi) inadequate information on their market;

vii) a limited range of potential providers from whom they can purchase;

viii) inadequate information through which to monitor their own 'purchasing' performance;

ix) inadequate ways of communicating with shareholders (its resident population) and, a 'noisy' channel of communication distorted by many other local political messages;

x)   little flexibility in the range of product lines it purchases;

xi) very little opportunity to change its 'liquidity' significantly, year on year.

CHANGING DEMANDS FROM DHAS

The DHAs will be held to account for the effectiveness of their use of their purchasing power. A crisp definition of success or failure in meeting 'health needs' is not, however, possible in the way that it is for a commercial company. Hence, much of the role of the DHA will be concerned with negotiating criteria for success, with its payers (the Region) and its shareholders (the resident population), which it believes it has the purchasing leverage to meet. For example, it should not be held to account for health deterioration arising from industrial diseases, or the provision of poor housing or road transport systems.

Once the DHA has acquired a package of performance measures which is acceptable to its sponsors, it will purchase such services from providers as will ensure a high performance in those areas. Hence, the service portfolio provided locally should change, with alteration in determination of services required.

The DHAs will have to spend resources on providing and acquiring the extra information necessary to manage their business – their market and performance in it. This leads to a reduction in the purchasing power of the DHA for 'direct patient care'. The performance criteria for the DHAs are unlikely to reduce commensurately, therefore the DHAs will be seeking constant improvements in efficiency from its provider sources. The service purchased and provided will be required to deliver new cost efficiencies year on year.

CHANGING DEMANDS ON DHAS

Influences on the activity of the DHAs will come from Region, general practitioners, consumers, consumer groups and the local authority. Each of these will have different views as to what constitutes the best balance between quality, cost and access in determining the best service portfolio to be acquired and maintained by the DHA.

The interests of the local providers (with whom a DHA as purchaser may place 70 per cent, 80 per cent, or even 90 per cent plus of its 'business') cannot be ignored in this complex balance of demands. The providers, however, have no overt responsibility to the collective patient interest groups for meeting the health needs of the resident population. Their prime motivating force is to 'satisfy' those people who interact with their service so that the consumers would wish to 'repeat' their purchase, and the payers would wish to renew their contracts with the provider. As a result, there are many different value systems impinging on the decision-making of the purchasers.

GENERAL PRACTICE FUND HOLDERS (GPFH) AS 'PAYERS'

General practice fund holders are the nearest equivalent in the NHS to the health maintenance organisations of the USA. There are significant differences, however. GPFHs receive their 'fixed' annual revenue from the government (via the Region) with which it is intended that they will either purchase or provide a specified range of services for the patients registered with them. There are important areas of flexibility in the limits on expenditure, including the fact that any patient who has had £5000 spent on him or her by the GPFH then becomes the 'financial responsibility' of the DHA of residence of the patient.

In order to 'prosper', the GPFH will wish to attract as many patients as can be accommodated, so as to increase the revenue allocation from Region and have a large income over which additional fixed costs can be spread. Therefore, GPFHs will be in competition with other providers for funds from Region.

92

CHANGING DEMANDS OF GPFH

GPFH will negotiate the best set of arrangements possible for their patients with the available set of possible providers. It is not known what balance will be struck between quality, cost and access for the future. The certainty is that perceptions will vary one to another, over time, and be different from the providers' desires or their perception of the best balance of service delivery.

Many will establish their own ability to undertake certain procedures currently purchased from a provider and 'buy' key provider personnel to deliver locally at their own premises, or in the patient's home. Hence, GPFHs can 'force' clinical changes on NHS providers.

GENERAL PRACTITIONERS AS 'COLLECTIVE' PATIENTS

In respect of the individual patient, the GP acts as a 'broker' or adviser in the same way as an insurance agent leads the consumer to the best deal with an insurace company, or a solicitor leads a client to the best barrister for that case.

In these patterns of relationship, historical preferences are often difficult to change. What is certain is that the providers will need to keep in close contact with such GPs so as to ensure that future referral patterns are advantageous to the provider.

MEMBERS OF THE PUBLIC AS INDIVIDUAL PATIENTS

In the world of the consumer-orientated market economy, many individual consumers make choices with very limited information. In health care, the knowledge of the consumer is even more scanty. However, consumers will have a growing influence on the behaviour of the 'payers' and so the providers have to be aware of what satisfies the consumers.

Individual patients will have little concern about cost, but will have expectations of improved quality and access. As a result, influencing the perceptions of the individual patient or prospective patient is an important activity. '

MANAGING FOR HEALTH RESULT

The definition of 'health result' will vary depending on who is making it.

Society at large may be concerned at achieving targets represented by 'Health For All 2000' or other national health/political priorities.

A local community may be concerned about particular aspects of the 'health status of the residents' or about availability of specific health services.

An individual will be concerned normally with the 'cure capability' of the local services with regard to his or her particular need.

A health provider will be concerned with ensuring the continuity of the organisation, 'health' in its financial affairs, in its structure and in the motivation of its staff.

The interaction of the interpretation of 'health result' at different levels, and the 'measurement of satisfaction' by different players, will yield a very complex set of expectations. There is a premium on all the players to define their contribution to the achievement of certain expectations very clearly. These contributions have to be negotiated with the interested parties thoroughly. The end result is that ideally for each player, 'payer, provider and patient', there should be two sets of commitments:

- an aggregation of a defined set of targets over which the organisation (or the individual) has control of the resources to deliver 'health results'; and

- individual or corporate contributions to improving the 'broader health status' of the community and society at large. (For example, this could involve individual efforts to adopt a healthy lifestyle, a corporate response to provide more screening services, more efficient care, or more housing)

RESPONSE OF THE PROVIDER

ASSUMPTIONS AND ANALOGIES

The 'provider' of the future will not have a captive market, nor an assurance of income. The most apt commercial analogies for the position of a 'provider' are as follows.

1. That of a producer with a very large product range, a highly technical market, only a few prime customers and a high fixed-cost business. In this case, the existence of a very large product range requires a business to achieve four capabilities (if it wishes to be successful):
   i)   as many common components as possible;
   ii) a detailed knowledge of costs in relation to the total price;
   iii) an efficient production flow line and mechanisms for controlling work-in-progress;
   iv) a constant review of the value of each product line to the health of the whole organisation and the willingnesses to delete those which do not contribute sufficiently.

   Operating in a highly technical market demands the following characteristics:
   i)   a great discipline in the production processes to assure the organisation of quality;
   ii) a preparedness to seek new methods and to implement them;
   iii) an ability to evaluate the benefits of new investment to the organisation and to select only those of most value.

   Operating with only a few prime customers demands that:
   i)   excellent relationships and communication are maintained at all levels between the provider and their purchasers;
   ii) the cost-base can be justified when seeking price increases;
   iii) the delivery performance meets expectations in both quality of the product and its availability.

   Operating in a high fixed cost business means that:
   i)   small changes in volume or variable cost at the margin can move the organisation rapidly between surplus and deficit;
   ii) tight control must be maintained on fixed costs;
   iii) opportunities to increase the proportion of the total costs which are truly variable must be sought with vigour.

2. The second analogy is that of an airline where the essential 'cog-in-the-wheel' is the highly trained and expensive airline pilot delivering a technical service which, to the customer, is felt in terms of outcome (personal service and tangible results of transport from A to B) within what is a high fixed-cost and competitive business. Here the essential points to register are:
   i)   the pilots have their basic work pattern well defined and are required to adhere to it. Opportunity for individual professional skills to be utilised exists during the in-flight situations;

ii) the consumer does not understand the technology of the business but makes a choice on quality, cost and access criteria (a familiar set of terms to health services around the world).

APPLICATION OF THE ANALOGIES

In considering the responses of the health care providers of the future the points raised from the commercial analogies above are helpful in pointing to key issues for health care provider organisations.

Product line consideration

The total set of activities undertaken by a health care provider must be split into health care groups. The flexibility of the management of each will be greatly enhanced if the hospital-based and community-based elements of care are integrated into them – (not easy in these days of separated Trusts).

Although the health care groups should be set up to define the strategy for each 'product line', the management control of all the components of care to deliver that 'product line', and, also to all the other 'product lines', is best achieved through functional control.

The concept of achieving common components is translated so as to retain strong departmental management within each clinical profession (and all the support professions). However, a proper contribution is made to each health care group (a product line) through a matrix management structure which enables internal commitments of resources to be made from each profession to each health care group.

Finally, each health care group is required to review regularly its whole strategy and to re-allocate resources to meet the new needs of its customers.

Health care providers have a variety of forms of customer. In the UK this will range from DHAs, GPFHs, ordinary GPs, individual patients, medical insurance companies and other statutory agencies (for example, local authorities). Health care providers will have to allocate direct financial resources and senior managers' time to the processes of establishing and maintaining excellent relationships with each group. A certain openness in information and costing will be required to enable the prime customers to accept the justification for claims for price increases.

The assurance that delivery performance meets expectations will underline the need for contracts (or service agreements) that are sufficiently explicit about aspects of performance, and the information systems to assure the provider that the contract is being fulfilled.

In a high fixed-cost business these three thrusts are vital. It is in these areas that the response of the health care providers will need to be positive if they are to survive. These areas are also difficult to achieve, as they address many clinical areas of vested interest and may challenge current employment practices.

The providers have competitors in the form of other providers and GPFHs. A provider could 'lose' 1 per cent to 5 per cent of income very easily. While this is a small percentage, because of the high fixed cost of staff and buildings and so on, a loss of £700,000 on a £70m income expectation is very significant.

Alternatively, purchasers may have around £100,000 to spend in the last three months of a financial year – 'hot money'. Providers will need to be able to 'gear-up' very quickly to take advantage of this extra revenue in an effective manner to meet the purchasers' demands. Flexibility can be seen as a key to success in the new NHS and for other health providers in the world.

Flexibility in how health care is delivered

Clinical practice and clinical prejudice have to be challenged and changed where it can be shown that an equivalent, or acceptable, outcome can be achieved at a lower cost. If the clinicians do not do this of their own accord, the Management Board (which should include clinicians) of the provider organisation will require both authority and strength of will to force a change.

This general thesis applies to all aspects of health care. Audit can be a prime vehicle for achieving such changes.

Flexibility in utilisation of facilities

In any flow of work, or in the delivery of a service, the system has to be designed to achieve the best balance possible. Efficiencies are gained when either the speed of the 'bottleneck' process is increased, or where 'work-in-progress' is reduced to a minimum through the achievement of reliable processes and a balanced relationship of throughputs. The Health Service has many different paths through it and is very complex. Nevertheless, there are instances of under-utilisation of facilities, or of ineffective use over extended periods.

A careful examination of the patient flow through the health care system will show inefficiencies. This has been done already in outpatients and in theatres in the UK.

One key to success is to enable clinicians to change their practices to maximise the utilisation of both their time and the facilities they require or draw upon.

Flexibility in employment practices

Changes in the use of facilities will require changes in the employment patterns of certain staff to ensure that staff availability is matched more closely to changes in the volume and/or mix of activity. Industry is well used to the employment of part-timers, twilight shifts, evening shifts, full 'continental' shifts and over-time. Health care providers will have to develop similar mechanisms.

Flexibility in the use of facilities

Purchasers of services may perceive a need to change significantly what is required to meet the health needs of their population.

The provider of services may also obtain extra work from other purchasers. Both these events may lead to the need for significant change in the use of outpatient facilities, wards, theatres or paramedic time. The clinicians involved will have to accept disruption to their normal pattern of work caused by the overarching needs of the whole organisation. The culture has to move away from a sense of 'ownership' of facilities by the clinicians, to one where they 'rent' the facilities to fulfill their personal contribution to service agreements with the purchasers.

KEY ISSUES FOR 'PROVIDERS'

The previous sections used commercial analogies to demonstrate particular ways in which 'providers' will have to respond in a 'market-style' Health Service. Many of the forms of response are already in place, or at least accepted widely as being essential – clinical audit for all professions, for example. I consider the following to be key issues for health care providers which arise from this comparison with commercial companies and their environment.

'INTERNAL' ISSUES: FLEXIBILITY

I would assert that the key issues internal to the 'providers' are:
i) Organise so as to integrate the planning of the package of care over the hospital and community aspects for each health care group – this maximises flexibility in response to the changes in health care.

ii) Change employment practices to create more flexibility in delivery of health care as this will be needed to respond to the changes in demand for, and practice of, health care.

iii) Create incentives to change clinical practice and the utilisation of facilities so as to encourage flexibility in meeting new demands for care and cost control.

iv) Direct more resources into creating the necessary information to support the organisation and into establishing contacts with the full range of external authorities, agencies and individuals who can influence the prosperity of the provider.

'EXTERNAL' ISSUES

The key issues 'external' to the providers derive from the previous analysis. While some of what I have said refers specifically to the Britain's NHS, the general issues probably have worldwide application. They are:

i) The 'providers' have to be prepared to change their service portfolio in response to the 'purchasers'' demands, and to continue to deliver cost efficiencies, year on year.

ii) The 'providers' have to be able to respond to significant changes in demand arising from competition with other providers and from changes in purchasing decisions arising from the different 'value system' of the purchasers.

iii) The 'providers' have to discover how to be pro-active in influencing the external decision-makers, opinion formers and in assessing the views of their patients.

Certainly in the UK, providers are not fully equipped in staff skills or in financial resources to undertake the consequences of issue iii) above. Yet this is vital if a 'market-like' system is to evolve.

'POLITICAL' ISSUES

The key differences between a commercial organisation and a health care provider (in the UK) is the former's ability to increase revenue significantly, and the latter's involvement with the moral issues of refusing access to services via a waiting list and restricted national funding. A commercial organisation can always work for an increased market share or to stimulate growth in the total market. By contrast, an NHS provider organisation operates within the 'zero-sum' game of a national (regional and district) cash-limited service. It is a political issue as to whether the 'total market' is allowed to grow; the 'provider' plays no part in this. If one provider succeeds in increasing market share, then others will be reducing their share, their income, their activity and it follows, their care.

This immediately leads into moral issues of refusing access to services in the 'losing' provider organisations. While this is essentially the responsibility of the 'purchaser', the public will perceive the failure to be the responsibility of the 'provider', so there is a premium on the 'providers' not losing business. All manner of devices will emerge to achieve this, which opens up the issue of motivation.

MOTIVATION

The motivators for commercial organisations were referred to previously as profitability, growth and liquidity, all of which lead to financial success for all involved.

In a cash-limited Health Service these have to be translated as financial balance, no increase in waiting lists, asset utilisation and cash management, all of which are summed up in the word 'survival'.

The threat of 'extinction' can be a motivator, but it does not sustain creative forces, associated with the commercial sector, being released into the health care sector. The solution, in my view, will be a two-tier service based on extra contributions (that is, payments) from individuals, or from some form of regional or local government (that is, increasing the purchasing power of the market locally through local taxes). In this way the total market can be made to grow at a rate, and in a direction, that is determined politically, at the local level. This is essentially what happens now in Canada.

How can we move fast when we haven't got the data?

(Editor)

In a complex world, we need information to guide our direction and help us evaluate our success. The problem has always been and remains how much of it do we really need, how good and how relevant is it, and how do we select the bits that are worth having? Dan Longo, as president of the Hospital Research and Educational Trust, contributed a detailed paper which linked a newly discovered role for quality with this still relevant problem.

100

THE USE AND MISUSE OF DATA: QUALITY AND COST IN POSSIBLE CONFLICT

DAN LONGO (UNITED STATES)

The major event during the 1980s was the public's transformation from 'patients' to 'health care consumers'. The consumer movements born in the 1970s spilled over to health care with the advent of spiralling costs, prospective reimbursement, and an increased percentage of the Gross National Product (GNP) devoted to health care. Exposures of therapeutic misadventures and allegations of poor facility conditions, like Medicine on Trial (1) and a Wall Street Journal (2) article on the dilapidated conditions of a Bronx hospital, caused a public outcry and encouraged the need for activism concerning the quality of health and medical care. Another phenomenon which has had an impact on health care is the importation of the quality focus that is the keystone of Japanese industry. In a related way, Peters and Waterman's *In Search of Excellence* (3) set the tone for the decade, so that concerns with quality in American business from cars to medical care increased exponentially.

To claim that quality in health care is important is stating the obvious. Yet, within the maelstrom of concerns that surround the system of care in United States, quality has rarely dominated. It does now. Avedis Donabedian writes:

After an interlude of forgetfulness during which we seem obsessed with how costly health care has become, and with how, for all our wealth, we were unable or unwilling to afford it, we are turning now to the one concern that should have always preoccupied us, the quality of care. (4)

These events manifested themselves in the hospital and medical care arena with concerns about 'outcomes'. This represents a shift in emphasis from concerns with the structure and process of care. At the same time,

---

(1) Inlander, C., Lowell, S. and Weiner, E. Medicine on Trial. Prentice Hall Press 1987.
(2) The Wall Street Journal. (11/13/89): 1
(3) Peters, T. and Waterman, R.H. In Search of Excellence. Harper Row 1982.
(4) Donabedian, A. Quality assessment and assurance: Unity of purpose, diversity of means. Inquiry. Spring 1988. 25:190.

health care providers have committed themselves to the improvement of the process: medical decision-making, content of care and technical skills are all involved (5). The proliferation of new diagnostic and therapeutic techniques, and the subsequent increase in choices, has created a movement by physicians and other providers to develop assessment and dissemination tools to ensure high quality. Internal quality assurance mechanisms, many of which were implemented out of cost concern, are beginning to evolve towards their stated purpose. There has also been an increase in external pressure on health care providers for accountability. Pressure from payers and the threat of litigation have increased awareness if not quality itself.

Payers – the third, besides patients and providers, of the general groups with interests in health care – have looked at quality under the auspices of cost effectiveness. The choice of individual services, the setting in which the services are delivered, and the frequency, timing and duration of care have all come under the scrutiny of the third party payers who are responsible for maximum care for least cost.

COST AND QUALITY – WHAT IS ON FIRST?

Of all these factors contributing to the emergence of quality, the influence of cost is the most important. Despite our enormous commitment to health care – 12 per cent of the national GNP – the health status of the average citizen of the United States lags behind that of most industrialised nations' peoples. Infant mortality in places like Washington D.C. approaches rates found in third world nations. Access to care is often reduced for the 37 million uninsured nationwide, and a good portion of our health resources are spent on heroic measures for those with less than two weeks to live. Small area analysis indicates that procedures that are well reimbursed are often performed in disproportionately large numbers, while trauma care centres and obstetrical units are being reduced due to staggering costs. The inevitable question then is raised: is the quality of United States' health care commensurate with the financial resources devoted to its delivery?

Quality, traditionally, has been viewed in a separate context from cost, with the expectation that decisions regarding health were in no way affected by financing. Consequently, the level of care was determined by

---

(5) US General Accounting Office: Quality Assurance: A comprehensive national strategy for health care is needed. February 1990. 6

the maximal effectiveness of the therapy. However, Avedis Donabedian, who first conceptualised the scheme of looking at quality through structure, process, and outcome, has emphasised that, like most products, there are decreasing marginal returns for health care. Given a situation in which resources are limited or scarce, the amount of care delivered would ideally be that at which marginal cost equals marginal benefit; this is called optimal effectiveness.(6) This thinking requires a change of paradigm, since society's claim on the health care dollar now affects individual patient care. The interconnectedness of quality and cost is manifested in the word 'value'. Value is defined as quality service for a reasonably price and is increasingly used in the same context as quality.

The maximally effective point is not one easily set. In addition to the disagreement among providers as to the theoretically ideal course of treatment or mix of services in an institution, there is the spectrum of patient preferences and values that contributes to the ambivalence. However, this difficulty is a fraction of that which occurs in the deliberations over the optimally effective amount of care. Tensions exist along the axes which connect patients, providers, and payers when cost considerations are factored into care decisions. The physician, for example, resents the adultering of the medical decision-making process by financial considerations. The purchaser of health care is pressured from both the consumer and provider to give more – more service, more reimbursement. And the consumer of health care often adopts the stance which is legitimised in other nations: health care is an entitlement. The strain on the system resulting from such disparate positions is partly responsible for the current fragmentation and complication that marks the delivery of care.

Thus far, a profile has been drawn which emphasises that the United States has a strong interest in quality, and that the interconnectedness of cost and quality has polarised the different populations involved in health care. Another dimension needs to be added – that of data. To use an expression coined by 'US News & World Report', Americans are data junkies. (7) In a society that deifies the objectivity of science, numbers are a crutch with which we extricate ourselves from hard-to-resolve conflicts.

THE DATA EXPLOSION

This phenomenon is occurring in health care. The nature and number of

---

(6) A. Donabedian as cited in Quality Management for Health Care Delivery. Chicago: HRET 1989, p. 23.
(7) Wattenberg, B.J. 'Beware the Data Twisters', in US News & World Report. 4/2/90.

requests for data have increased at a rate faster than that of the costs of care. The purposes for the data vary, ranging from evaluation of clinical diagnoses, risk assessment, marketing among competitive providers and cost control. In fact, a recent report of the Institute of Medicine's study of quality in the Medicare programme concludes that 'the multiplicity of external review activities we have observed throughout this study results in unacceptable duplication of resources, and considerable frustration on the part of providers. (8).

The 1970s saw private, third-party insurers engaging in the process of utilisation review due to their high costs and fear of fraudulent or faulty care. Since then, a wide array of groups for an equally wide array of reasons have taken to the data democracy. There are seven different sorts of inquirers: private and public purchasers and payers; accrediting, certifying, licensing agencies; federal, state, regional, and local regulators; consumers and consumer groups; private and public data agencies; private and public researchers; and other private groups such as utilisation review management companies and malpractice insurers. While many of the requests and efforts of these groups are understandable given their use, several key problems exist that undercut the function of data.

First, there is the nature of the data currently used. Most of the data applied to quality assessment was collected for billing purposes. Billing statistics can be considered the grossest of the data collected on individual patients with regard to quality, since it represents a simple codification of diagnoses and co-morbidities. Only at the level of medical charts and the physiological data, such as lab results, is the clinical detail sufficient for true assessment of quality. These financial data also suffer from doubts about reliability and validity.

An example of the dangers of data without context or clear methods for use is the mortality data releases. Beginning in 1986, hospital-specific mortality data for 16 diagnostic clusters were published, with high public interest and low public understanding. Because the initial data were unadjusted, hospitals treating more severely ill patients were juxtaposed to those with more health populations, leading to false impressions about the relative quality of the institutions.

A second problem with the data demand is the data 'burden' that comes from information requested that a) is not ordinarily gathered, or b) is collected but not processed, analysed or reported in the requested format. The great number of parties concerned with health care data place demands that are exorbitant and unco-ordinated. In addition, the type of data or information that employers, employer coalitions and other

(8) Lohr, K.N. (ed.). A Strategy for Quality Assurance. Washington: Institute of Medicine 1990, p. 319.

purchasers require is constantly changing. The already constricted resources of care providers must be funnelled toward responding to these requests. On the providers' side, there are no standards for the organisation and presentation of the information. Consequently, communication between information requestor and provider is marred.

Perhaps the most powerful criticism levelled at the data explosion is the misuse of data. There is little understanding on the part of the recipients of the data of the nuances displayed, and few educational opportunities for them.

There is intense pressure from the public, third-party insurers and industry to release hospital- and physician-specific mortality data, yet without an appreciation for the meaning and derivation of these numbers, they will not only lose their usefulness, they will be misrepresentative.

The misuse of data can more specifically be nailed to the different perceptions of quality. The patient, provider and payer would expect different information because of their unique definitions of quality.

INFORMATION: DATA THAT WORKS

These three problems – the nature of the data, the format for reporting and requesting data, and its misuse – are listed here, not in disparagement, but in acknowledgement that these are the first issues that need to be resolved on the road to effective quality improvement efforts. In fact, initiatives have already begun to address them. The Utilization Review Accreditation Commission has developed the 'National Utilization Review Standards' which, among other things, prescribes uniform formats for requesting data elements. (9)

The transformation of data into information is crucial to the attempts to harness the concern for quality into meaningful action. Data is defined as abstract representations of reality that have been stored on a passive medium. Information is data translated into statements that are useful for decision-making. This means that data, in the absence of meaningful definitions of quality and means for decision-making and action, is functionless. Data becomes information only when located within some framework for its appreciation and use.

Avedis Donabedian broadly states that quality 'consists in the ability to achieve desirable objectives using legitimate means.' (10) As seen in the plurality of the American health care system and in the variety of perceptions of quality of care, there is no single objective for quality. Rather than struggle to find the ultimate objective, a more worthwhile

---

(9) **Hospital Peer Review. 19 June 1990. p. 90.**
(10) **Donabedian, A. Inquiry, p. 173.**

activity might be to construct a framework within which dialogue between payers, patients and providers could occur. This approach would not attempt to eliminate conflict, but would aggregate the various desires and needs so, at the least, miscommunication would be reduced. At the most, prioritisation of needs, co-ordination of efforts and co-operation in quality improvement activities would take place. An example of the data elements that might come under such an umbrella include clinical outcome indicators and practice guidelines for physicians; cost-effectiveness and technology assessment information for payers; and patient satisfaction indicators to reflect the concerns of the general public.

As well as the refinement of the framework for data use in quality, practical methods for the implementation of quality improvement mechanisms need enhancement.

There are obviously a variety of questions that require attention. Among these are the following:

- Is some data better than no data at all?

- What are the cost/quality trade-offs?

- What data should be collected?

- How should the data be defined, collected, reported, analysed and used?

- Who controls the data?

- What safeguards must be taken to protect patient and hospital confidentiality?

- Will data increase the cost of hospital care?

- Will data increase the quality of hospital care?

- Should a public, private or shared public-private data utility be created?

It is anticipated that these questions must be addressed in our attempt as a society to be responsible in our use of hospital data. In the process, we must exercise caution. As US News and World Report states:

Beware. We are in an unprecedented era of data twisting. Of course, statistics are not set in stone. Definitional problems alone can lead honourable people to come to different conclusions ... We end up governed by social fictions, not by social facts. As the data soon start flying, the public should ask the lawyer's question: Cui Bono? Who gains? (11)

The internal market:
the challenge to NHS providers
(Editor)

Frank Burns continues to inspect the reality of making change happen, also within the British context, noting, rather gloomily, the failures of the so-called 'earlier reorganisations' to make much impact on anything. As he comments, the NHS has adopted a bureaucratic response to resolving tensions. What is now needed is a much more managerial and pro-active model, along the lines suggested in this book. Interestingly, he sees the challenge to the managers of provider institutions as both testing and important.

(11) Wattenberg, B.J. 'Beware the Data Twisters' in US News and World Report. 4/2/90.

MEETING THE CHALLENGE TO DELIVER QUALITY

FRANK BURNS (UNITED KINGDOM)

Throughout its history the National Health Service has consistently struggled in its attempts to strike a successful balance between supporting existing service provision and responding to the changing needs of the population. The purchaser/provider model is the most recent organisational attempt to do this.

Changes in the organisation of UK health care are now enshrined in the NHS and Community Care Act 1990 – at their heart a determination to bring about organisational and statutory separation of local health authorities (purchasers) from previously subordinate operational units (providers). The intention and the undoubted effect of this change will be to resolve at a stroke the organisational and philosophical conflicts arising from the incorporation of responsibility for existing operational services (providers) and responsibility for determining community needs and bringing about change (the purchaser role) within the same organisational entity. The new arrangements are intended to achieve the following:

1. The creation of a genuinely separate purchasing organisation with clearly focused responsibility for assessing, measuring and prioritising health care needs of defined populations.

2. Organisational (and preferably statutory) independence for NHS providers.

3. The use of service agreements or contracts between purchasers and providers as the mechanism through which purchasers and providers reach explicit understandings on the relationship between service cost, volume and quality.

4. An obligation on purchasers to maximise services available to their resident population through comparing the efficiency of different providers and arranging contracts if necessary with different providers on a value for money basis.

108

THE CHALLENGE TO NHS PROVIDERS

The managerial autonomy conferred on providers, coupled with the creation of the internal market, presents the most significant test of the quality of hospital/provider management in the history of the National Health Service. NHS provider managers have a very short time indeed to adapt to the new environment and culture created by the separation of the purchaser role. There are a number of fundamental changes in their operating environment:

The purchaser role

The release of purchasers from operational obligations will allow them to focus all their energies on developing the skills and expertise necessary for the task of assessing health care needs of the resident population and the relationship between those prioritised needs and the existing range of provision. As purchaser expertise in epidemiology and analysis of current utilisation increases, the disparities, discrepancies, anomalies and the blatant unfairness of current patterns of service provision will become more obvious and will have to be tackled.

If the purchasers do not grasp the nettle of health care priorities and equitable access then they have no role at all. For the life of the NHS, service planners have been frustrated by the overwhelming dominance of operational professionals and they now have an ideal opportunity to put their skills and ambitions to good use on behalf of those needs of the local population which have not been addressed sufficiently well under the old regime.

There are still considerable practical and political constraints on purchasers' ambitions for radical change, but it is inevitable that providers will be dealing with purchasers who are much more assertive in pressing their intentions for changes to priorities and patterns of service.

The service agreement (or contract)

Throughout the life of the NHS, billions on billions of pounds have been made available to hospitals and other provider units with virtually no specification or detailed agreement between the funding authority and the hospitals.

This is not to suggest that district health authorities have been unaware of the use to which funds were put. Indeed, if anything, there has been an excessive preoccupation with what the money was spent on and almost no debate on the quality of the process and outcomes of care. To illustrate the

109

point, it is a fact that the vast majority of district health authorities concern themselves only with the overall numbers of patients waiting for surgery but have no idea of specific conditions on a waiting list.

Access to facilities has been determined solely at the professional level and the funding authority has had neither the information, inclination or opportunity to have a real influence on utilisation of resources at the patient level.

The creation of the purchaser role and the emphasis on specification through service agreements will introduce a more demanding regime. Purchasers will set down in a much more explicit way their expectations in relation to service volume, quality and cost.

In addition, while negotiating, purchasers are liable to be more aggressive in the pursuit of increased efficiency at the provider level. Of course, purchasers will not have it all their own way. One objective of the new arrangements is the creation of circumstances where the best use of available resources in the interests of the local community can be determined. It must be recognised, however, that from the perspective of the provider and especially health care professionals, it is the funding agencies that have suppressed the focus on quality over the years through their preoccupation with volumes and efficiency. Where providers are statutorily independent of purchasers they will doubtless wish to exploit this independence to press their own claims for improved quality of service and will not easily yield to the notion that, after ten continuous years of cost improvement targets and underfunded inflation, improved quality can be achieved through more efficiency. Providers will doubtless be using their new status as equal partners in the negotiation to remind purchasers that 'they cannot have their cake and eat it'.

The internal market

Health care professionals at operational level have taken for granted the continued local need for their service. This is due, in part, to the cumbersome and inflexible financial systems and lack of information which tended to support historical patterns of provision. Other factors include the absence of any specific or explicit agreement on standards of care against which the performance of professionals could be measured and, in part, also to the reluctance of general practitioners to use objective criteria for choice of hospital referral.

The creation of the separate purchaser role basis coupled with the introduction of fund holding general practitioners will create an environment where providers cannot take their traditional patient flows for granted. Purchasers and general practitioners will, in future, compare the performance of different providers against cost and quality criteria before placing contracts for those particular services which are amenable to such a process (principally elective surgery). This introduces a powerful incentive for the eradication of provider complacency concerning patient flows, service quality and all round efficiency.

The introduction of limited competition between hospitals where cost is a factor in the decision imposes an immediate and comprehensive requirement for analysis of patient costs to an extent that is currently not available in any NHS hospital. The deficiency is well illustrated by the fact that, for some years to come, cost comparisons between one hospital and another will be at the level of modified average specialty costs which embrace such an enormous range of specific conditions that they are virtually useless for all but the most crude form of comparison.

MANAGING THE CHANGE

Despite what will inevitably prove to be a much more demanding and rigorous operating environment for NHS providers than anything previously experienced, most provider managers are enthusiastic supporters of the separation of the purchaser/provider role. This arises from an acceptance and understanding among them that the price they must pay for genuine operational autonomy is the creation of powerful and effective purchasing agencies. Over time, they will seek to adjust the balance between hospital and other forms of health care, between professional and public aspirations for service development and between traditional and more efficient patterns of provision.

Provider managers and increasing numbers of health care professionals recognise the legitimacy of such changes given the inexhaustible nature of the demand for health care and the limited availability of resources. The task now is to introduce and manage the change processes necessary to equip both the people and the organisation for the new environment. Bearing in mind the size and complexity of large hospitals, the relatively entrenched position of many professionals and the significant degree of hostility to the changes, the scale of the change management process should not be underestimated. Among the many major issues to be tackled by provider managers in readiness for the changes, the following could be regarded as the most significant.

Commitment to the changes

It must be acknowledged that not everybody who works in hospitals is fully or even remotely in tune with the conceptual arguments in favour of the separation of the purchaser and provider role. Many see the process merely as an inadequate alternative to making more resources available for health care while others maintain an overtly political stance against the government introducing the change. Others see the creation of independent hospitals, even within the National Health Service, as the thin end of a wedge and as a potential threat to the principle of public sector provision of health care. All such reactions are a manifestation of natural resistance to change and inevitable anxiety when change takes on a radical form. Senior managers throughout the whole of the NHS have an enormous challenge before them in winning hearts and minds in relation to the need for and benefits of the proposed changes – the value issue already noted.

Internal organisation

This is an important area on which hospital managers will need to focus. Hospitals will be required, in the future, to provide services to a much more rigorous and exacting standard than hitherto, especially in relation to such factors as cost and quality. Purchaser expectations will be specified in formal service agreements. This requires a structure which generates commitment to and accountability for its satisfaction.

Clinical professional staff in hospitals until recently took a very limited interest in, or responsibility for, the relationship between work done, quality achieved and resources available. In its crudest manifestation, hospital management took the form of professional managers using a variety of control techniques to constrain overall expenditure against an annual cash limit without having any effective mechanisms, structures or processes for establishing a connection between work done and resources used at the sub-unit level.

Across the country in recent years a number of experiments have been conducted based on the concept of clinical directorates headed by senior consultant staff with a remit to assess the practicability of reconciling the professional imperative of clinical freedom with the organisational imperative of efficient resource management. Evidence from pilot sites, not surprisingly, suggests that there is considerable benefit to be gained from a formal involvement of senior clinical professional staff in the management of resources at the sub-unit level. This benefit is not manifest only in improved control of finances (which, in fact, has yet to be demonstrated) but more particularly in the creation of corporate ownership and identity at the specialty level. The clinical directorate is providing an ideal vehicle for the formulation of service specifications, quality standards, activity analysis, medical audit, clinical audit, financial analysis and most importantly of all, the pursuit of improved service quality.

It is difficult to see how providers will be in any position to give commitments to purchasers on detailed service agreements without an internal structure which clearly identifies accountability for the management and execution of the contracts. Clinical directorates can provide one mechanism for achieving this. Their establishment is an immensely demanding task requiring a considerable effort of organisational development.

Corporate image and customer orientation

It will be particularly important for NHS providers to exploit their separation from the NHS bureaucracy for the purposes of building up workforce commitment to corporate objectives and culture. The notion of independent provider units provides an ideal opportunity to harness the vast reservoir of loyalty and commitment that hospital staff have for the hospital at which they work. This, in recent years, has been undermined by a resentful attitude to the wider NHS bureaucracy. The task of reversing these attitudes is, of course, linked to the hearts and minds effort referred to above, but most specifically requires a commitment to the notions of quality and efficiency as a means of guaranteeing continued purchaser loyalty to the current range of service and the development of new services.

A particular need exists to develop a customer orientation among NHS staff not just in relation to individual patient contact but for all those areas where a customer relationship exists, for example, between the hospital as a whole and its various purchasers, between consultants and general practitioners, between clinical directorates and service departments, between professionals and individual patients.

For a whole variety of reasons over recent years, NHS staff working at hospital level in all disciplines and at all levels have developed a degree of cynicism about the motives and intentions of the wider NHS bureaucracy and this has served to undermine commitment to the pursuit of excellence and success. In some senses this has served to produce an impression of indifference to the objectives of the hospital and acceptance of mediocre and inadequate services. Provider managers in the NHS face a particularly important challenge in eradicating apathy and generating a high performance, high quality and success orientated culture.

CONCLUSION

The NHS and Community Care Act of 1990 introduced the most radical cultural and organisational change ever faced by NHS managers. From the provider point of view the changes will create an immeasurably more exacting management environment through the enhanced power of purchasers, through the introduction of explicit service agreements, and through the introduction of a more business-like financial regime. The need to respond to the challenges of this new environment will unquestionably provide an unprecedented impetus for fundamental improvements in the processes and quality of operational health care management.

The creation of an effective purchaser role in health care should bring direct benefits to the wider community. The improvement in the quality of hospital management which must follow will most certainly produce direct and significant benefits for hospital patients.

Comment
(Editor)

I am a little pessimistic about how far senior actors in health care can really learn the fast and flexible message. This gloom is based less on our conference, and more on working within the British National Health Service and visiting the United States. There may be a connection with the whole idea of professionals – a subject in its own right already much researched. The very nature of a profession, with its established rules, procedures, precedents and behaviours, does not lend itself easily to a pro-active, relaxed and flexible form of managerialism. The struggle continues and it is certainly unclear where it might go. However, as all our economies continue to decline, and our populations to age, there can be no return to the old ways. As in war, traditional values and barriers are likely to break down – whether this will ultimately be for good or ill is unclear.

THE F PLAN PART III: FRIENDLY CO-OPERATION AND COLLABORATION

Health care delivery is about caring, so clearly we are all carers and are therefore friendly! In truth, this is far from the case. It is easy to find individuals who could start a fight in an empty room, and groups wandering around in the hope of encountering a conflict, or starting one.

If we then imagine everyone moving flexibly at speed while continuing to act in a hostile and unfriendly fashion, it is apparent that emergency rooms will be even more full. I once observed an infants' school, where I was a governor, exercising its inmates. One class had a reputation for disruptive behaviour and hostility and a teacher who seemed intent on keeping things that way. Playtime was a nightmare – all the children crashed into one another, tripped each other up, fights broke out and the fragile and vulnerable wept quietly on the sidelines. The next class came out – same age – with a reputation for friendliness and co-operation, and equally, a teacher intent on keeping it that way. There was the same amount of rushing around, lots of energy was burnt up, many games took place, but no-one was hurt and no-one cried. If we are to speed up organisational processes we have to do so in a climate of warmth and trust, or we will simply make a mess faster. Friendliness is hard and friendship harder. Human psychology and organisations often seem better at hostility. To build real alliances which stand up to tests is hard work – much more laborious than conflict and, paradoxically, often less fun – or certainly less exciting! The following papers look at cases where alliances worked, and others where conflict reigned.

Firstly, Steve Herbert presents us with a case study of organisational change. The background to his work had two themes. Firstly, Ontario had been described in 1985 as a system which was 'least under control' (1). In addition, within the province, statistics showed that elderly people were institutionalised at a higher rate than either in Canada as a whole or in countries such as the United Kingdom. Within this context, a long-term reform programme began in 1989 to attempt both to bring the system under financial control and to provide appropriate care for elderly people.

---

(1) Kane, R.A., Kane, R.L. Self care and health in old age. Crom Helm 1986. (page 103

115

It can be seen that potential for conflict between these goals and among various organisations was high.

In making these changes, the lead players recognised in advance the potential for conflict and avoided it by adopting strategies based on co-operation. Although this in itself is no guarantee of success, it at least ensures that all parties are committed to achieving a maximisation of outcomes.

RECONCILING INCOMPATIBLE OBJECTIVES IN REFORMING CARE FOR ELDERLY PEOPLE

STEVE HERBERT (CANADA)

Ontario's long-term care system for elderly people is dominated by institutions, with little provision for co-ordination. It also consumes a high proportion of total resources. Fragmentation and duplication of services are common criticisms. The governmental payers' goal in introducing long-term care reform is to build 'a coherent and integrated system' on the basis of existing services, within the context of financial constraint.

THE PROCESS FOR INTRODUCTION OF LONG-TERM CARE REFORM

In June of 1989, Ontario's minister of community and social services announced that an inter-ministry task force had been established with a mandate to reform the long-term care system. The ministries involved included Health (MOH) and Community and Social Services (MCSS) – the two major payers in the system – and two others with responsibility for Disabled Persons and Senior Citizens' Affairs. Seven principles to guide reform were also announced.

In December of 1989, the minister of community and social services presented a progress report to the Ontario legislature which identified five commitments:

- creation of new service access agencies

- introduction of a new funding system for nursing homes and homes for aged people

- establishment of an inter-Ministry structure (between MOH and MCSS) to manage the system

- development of an integrated in-home support programme (for example, providing homemaking and personal care services) for disabled people and seniors

- expansion of home support programmes (for example, meals on wheels, friendly visiting) run by community agencies (Government of Ontario, 1989).

Following the December announcement, the Ministries began a process of actively soliciting service provider and consumer input. A number of committees were set up to advise on specific programme development initiatives and the reform process in general. The provincial budget delivered in April of 1990 included funding for the development of long-term care reform.

The Government released a document outlining strategies for long-term care reform in May of 1990. It was intended to serve as a basis for community discussion over the summer of 1990 and to provide the framework for further development.

The Ministries have chosen seven underlying principles to guide reform:

- Services are to be tailored to meet the needs of individuals. This requires flexibility and responsiveness.

- The right of individuals to exercise choice and maintain their independence must be protected.

- Services should assist individuals to remain in their own homes and communities whenever possible.

- Consumers are to have easy access to the services they need.

- The role of informal caregivers should be complemented and sustained by the formal care system.

- Local planning and management is to be maximised within a framework of provincial standards and policy directions.

- The system must make effective use of resources to meet needs within provincial fiscal policy and provide for a fair sharing of costs between government and consumers (Government of Ontario, 1990).

Although each of these principles is laudable when considered individually, some are likely to conflict with or limit others. For example, anyone with severe cognitive and physical functional impairment can be cared for at home given sufficient human and financial resources. Thus, the principle of maintaining people at home will in some cases conflict with the meeting of needs 'affordably' within provincial fiscal policy. Experience with the deinstitutionalisation of elderly people in Britain has led to the realisation that community care is not necessarily less expensive than institutional alternatives, although it may be more cost-effective.

The hierarchy of priority attached by governmental payers to each of the principles will emerge as long-term care reform is implemented. If 'affordability' becomes the overriding principle, there is a significant probability that consumers will react negatively. Opinion surveys of Canadians have consistently shown that, as a population, we feel strongly about maintenance of our health care system, including long-term care services. Government spending in this sector is given higher priority by the public than most other sectors, with the possible exception of the environment. Approximately 48 per cent of those polled in a March 1990 survey felt that health care spending is less than adequate. The same survey also indicated little support for decreasing services to senior citizens as a means for decreasing health care costs.

Recognising the realities of the political environment and listening to what 'the public' really wants, can help to keep the protagonists focused – and willing to change previously established views or positions.

Threats and friendliness
(Editor)

A common discussion topic during the conference was how far it was necessary to have significant external stimuli – usually threats – to ensure effective organisational system change. Donald Schurman's paper suggests that various tensions among players, providers and users in the context of fiscal difficulty and altering values provided a unique opportunity to influence the future delivery of health care. It also enables us to move into the field of quality improvement programmes and to consider how far they are simply a passing fad and, on the other hand, how far they may be a genuine way of enabling people of diverse values and backgrounds to focus in a 'friendly' fashion so as to attain desired outcomes.

119

USING QUALITY IMPROVEMENT AS A SYSTEMATIC PROCESS FOR SHARPENING INSTITUTIONAL PERFORMANCE COMMENT

DON SCHURMAN (CANADA)

INTRODUCTION

There are two main conditions for successful system movement. One is when there is a budget feast; then change can be 'bought'. The other is when there is a budget famine, when change becomes inevitable. Perhaps, in this era of restraint, improvements in our health care system, good as we know it to be, can be made. Vision, political will and co-operation among all participants are the basic requirements.

The University of Alberta Hospitals (UAH), of which I am the President, have selected a quality improvement process as a means of responding to these environmental pressures and the need for change, within a period of relative budget famine.

CURRENT OBJECTIVES OF THE QUALITY IMPROVEMENT PROCESS

Objectives of our quality initiative for the first year of 1990 were relatively modest. We have focused our efforts on three critical areas; awareness, skills and process. Awareness has been, and continues to be, accomplished through Board and senior management presentations, improving service/quality workshops for all employees, and quality improvement orientations conducted at all levels of the organisation. Improving individual employee skills is at the heart of our quality initiative. A recent training needs analysis indicated few deficiencies in the area of technical training. Our weakness is in the area of quality improvement, problem solving, quality measurements, customer listening, personal coaching and team skills. These deficiencies are being addressed. In the next training phase, statistical quality and process control techniques will be introduced.

Finally, the process for continuous quality improvement in the UAH has been the development of a functional structure to drive the quality initiative, primarily guided by the Quality Improvement Council.

CORPORATE QUALITY IMPROVEMENT INITIATIVES

Concurrent with the overall objectives of awareness, skills and process, the Quality Improvement Council has been working on four corporate quality improvement initiatives. The first of these initiatives or themes is the development of a customer listening process. The Quality Improvement Council identified their major customers as rural and urban physicians, and inpatients and outpatients. Four quality improvement task forces have been established to elicit from representatives of each customer group, their expectations of the UAH, and the extent to which they believe these expectations are being met. Each task force will devise indicators and measurement systems that can track the progress in meeting and exceeding their customers' needs and expectations. It is intended that the customer listening process will eventually include all divisions and departments in the UAH.

The second corporate quality improvement initiative involves the establishment of a macro quality measurement system. In an attempt to understand better the performance of the organisation as a whole, the Quality Improvement Council identified 12 key quality indicators. These indicators include, for example, employee turnover rates, admissions to hospital when the patient was in the hospital emergency department 24-hours prior to admission and waiting list trends. The Quality Improvement Council believes that these key indicators, measured and reported on a regular basis, will provide a relatively accurate reading of the overall rating of the hospitals.

The third corporate quality improvement initiative is the development of a quality improvement pilot study on three 18-bed surgical nursing units. Since all departments relate to nursing units in one way or another, departments will also have a role to play in this pilot project. All components of the quality improvement programme will be implemented on the three nursing units. With this pilot study it is anticipated that staff will begin to understand their role in the quality improvement process and, as they learn, it is expected that the quality improvement programme will gradually be introduced to all nursing units.

The fourth corporate initiative includes the development of departmental/divisional work process studies. As a preliminary step in this initiative, the Quality Improvement Council has identified a corporate-wide

121

issue which needs to be addressed – the scheduling of meetings. A quality improvement team has been established to examine the process in depth and to make recommendations on strategies to streamline and standardise an effective approach for scheduling meetings throughout the hospitals.

Once these four corporate initiatives are developed, refined, and in place for some time, it is anticipated that the quality improvement 'culture' will become internalised by all employees, volunteers and medical staff throughout the UAH.

THE FUTURE OF QUALITY IMPROVEMENT

The UAH recognises that quality improvement is not a quick fix but rather, a way of life. Where then is the UAH headed on this quest for quality?

NOW	FIVE YEARS FROM NOW
Incomplete understanding of customer requirements.	Use of systematic approach to understanding and satisfying both internal and external customer requirements.
Short term objectives and actions with limited long-term perspective.	Deliberate balance of long range goals with successive short term objectives.
Acceptance of a margin of error and subsequent corrective action as the norm.	Striving for continuous improvement in error-free output in meeting or exceeding customer requirements.
Unstructured, individualistic problem solving and decision making.	Predominantly participative and disciplined problem solving and decision making using a common approach.
Management style with uncertain objectives that instill fear of failure.	An open style with clear and consistent objectives which encourages problem solving and group-derived solutions.
Department management of services.	Cross-functional management of services.
Limited medical and employee involvement in the planning, implementation and evaluation of services.	Fuller participation of medical staff and employees in planning, implementation and evaluation of services.
Limited community and vendor involvement.	Partnership in developing health care services, educational programmes and conducting research.
Results oriented for management only.	Process management that focuses on work process not merely procedure.
Fragmented measurement.	Systematic measurement, statistical thinking and statistical quality control.
Minimal employee training.	Quality training for all employees and medical staff.

CONCLUSION

The introduction of continuous quality improvement in the UAH poses a significant challenge as well as a unique opportunity to manage the rising tensions among patients, employees and management. Over time, it is expected that continuous quality improvement will embrace the organisation and fundamentally change the way in which the UAH is managed.

Quality improvement provides an expanded foundation for generating a consensus among payers, providers and customers as to the future of the health care delivery system. The recognition of its relevance will enhance that system. Its implementation will be the future challenge for health care administrators.

The wheel has been invented
(Editor)

As already mentioned, the conference took place against a background of unavoidable change within health care systems, driven by the necessities of the wider political environment. In particular, the differences between the United States and the United Kingdom were often used as examples of two extremes, in the interesting context of each trying to move closer to the other. One of the ways of improving any system is to learn from others – and to provide friendly and co-operative ways in which this can be done. Fred Alley's paper, written from the perspective of the United States' system and the dominance of providers, sets out neatly some of the dilemmas facing such a system for those of us in other countries seeking to move towards more market orientated principles. In the course of it there are many tips and ideas which can be used by the key players, and I have thus quoted the paper fairly extensively. What is not shown is the fair amount of data which Fred used to support some of his arguments – any reader interested in obtaining a copy should contact me.

ADVICE ABOUT MARKETS IN HEALTH CARE AND THEIR REGULATORS

FRED ALLEY, UNITED STATES

Jim Bailey, president and chief executive officer of Broadway Hospital and Medical Centre in New York City, had to plan what to say about financing, quality controls and the evolving practices of management and governance that came with the stronger and stronger competition among his institutional neighbours. He had the opportunity to do so to one of the key players in NHS planning.

He was aware of recent changes in the British National Health Service that were vigorously debated both before and after the publication of *Working for Patients* (1). The literature and discussion he had heard or read was from the perspective of aggregate cost and health outcome effect.

Since 1948 the National Health Service had directly delivered medical care to all when it was needed, and, with few exceptions, without any charge to the patient – a system of delivery funded by general progressive taxes and providing universal coverage. Investor or private hospitals were a small component of the nation's service capacity. The vast majority of hospital service was provided by public hospitals run by district health authorities. The DHA receives a block grant from the Government to carry out its work for defined geographic and demographic areas; a monopoly delivery system under one set of operations, guidelines and financing.

Independent general practitioners, paid partly through what American physicians would recognise as capitation from the NHS, and other private service revenues provided primary care. These physicians served as gatekeepers for all hospitalisation except emergency services. Was there a different balance between inappropriate procedures because doctors did not get more for doing more procedures and the potential of missed procedures from the same incentive? Seventy-five per cent of all health service episodes began and ended with the GP. No wonder health costs in England consumed half as much of their gross national product as the American system.

In January 1989, the British Government issued a restructuring plan for the National Health Service entitled *Working for Patients*. DHAs would be

(1) United Kingdom Department of Health. Working for Patients. Command No. CM555. HMSO London 1989.

transformed from providers of health services to payers of health services. Geographic and demographic monopoly within the districts would give way with each DHA encouraged to find the best quality and the best price even should that be in another DHA district or from non-NHS providers. The DHA would receive its grant from the Government based on a formula that attempted to account for the size of an age-adjusted population and other factors such as illness history. Historically, DHAs received an adjustment for the flow of people in or out of the DHAs area. In future, this too would be accommodated by direct payment, one DHA to the pertinent provider. NHS hospitals could apply to leave DHA control and become independent, self-governing NHS Trusts. These Trusts could set their own arrangements with their employees and then compete for any and all patients that they were capable of serving. This was coupled with the concern for quality. The administration of the new system was already creating the declared need for quality assurance procedures and monitors to be developed.

The American system, with its public, private, and voluntary hospitals might lend itself to some insights as to how policy can both be achieved and indirectly threatened.

- Often data is not defined, collected, or reported in a consistent manner for comparison across systems, regions or countries. This holds true for States within the federal system in the United States.

- Health outcome is an analytical application that is not fully developed and difficult to use in international comparisons.

- In addition to medical and health service variables, the differences across cultures, social structure and expectations, demographic differences and economic differences between countries make comparisons difficult to identify cause and effect.

- Policy as a political process differs between countries. This makes policy formulation, implementation, and ultimate feasibility a variable in itself in international discussions.

HEALTH SERVICE COSTS – PRESENT AND FUTURE

Jim doubted the relative ability of hospital efficiency to contribute to the reduction of projected costs of health care services. He consulted tables of data and discovered various contrasts.

The UK cost in 1960 had been about 4 per cent compared to the United States' 5.5 per cent. While the US had a steady increase from 1960 to the 1980s, Britain's cost grew approximately 2 per cent in the 1970s and has remained relatively stable. While the two countries differed by 1.5 per cent in 1960, the difference was close to double in 1986. In addition, the UK had achieved universal coverage of its citizens, an unachieved goal in the US.

A distinguishing feature of American health financing was the private sources of payment, usually directly from insurers on behalf of the employed and paid for by the employer. Often the public debate in the US centred upon the public dollar. This was changing, with business clearly aware that more than their profit margins were at stake if projected national health expenses were not abated. Graphics based on data supplied by the Federal government had suggested heavy increases in expenditure.

The Social Security Administration projections for the end of the century included increases of one-third for each five-year period. Could this scale of increased costs come out of efficiency within the system? Given data as a relative contribution by public and private sources at the same time, the relative proportion of public and private cost was amazingly stable.

By the end of the century, it was projected that some $US5500 would be spent on each man, woman, and child, with over $US3000 of that commitment coming from private sources.

Little more than 10 per cent of cost growth was explained by population, and that approximately one-third of the change was economy-wide and not directly influenced by the hospital. Another one-third was explained probably by the nature of the population, its age and the incidence of illness. Finally, about one-fifth of the cost increase was attributable to physician, nursing home, hospital, and other structural elements of medical service. The aging and chronic conditions evolving as a larger proportion of hospitalised people was a very real trend. It meant that private funds would be carrying more and more of this burden as people continued to move into older age groups. It also set the stage for the argument that the longer people live and work, the more episodes of illness they will have. All of this dynamic change occurs with or without an efficient or consumer-orientated health care delivery system.

THE FORCES OF COMPETITION AND THE VALUES OF PUBLIC HEALTH POLICY PUT AT RISK

If hospitals are attempting to offer low prices to a payer, they may feature clinical programmes that are low in cost leaving more tertiary depth unavailable.

'Skimming' patients was an issue discussed often in the mid-1970s. Hospitals allegedly provided only services that did not require complex diagnostic and treatment modalities or time in hospital that adds to costs of care. In this way, they could apply themselves to low cost procedures and take those cases away from another hospital committed to a larger spectrum of services. This could reduce the ability of that more committed hospital to meet its expenses.

Conversely, in some areas, competition triggers a proliferation of tertiary programmes (and their technology and staffing) as hospitals attempt to compete for patients and physician referrals (see also London teaching hospitals pre-Tomlinson!).

If the nature of the competition is driven by the concern of the GP that the patient will receive the full diagnostic and treatment resources, they may be reluctant to make referrals to a hospital that has attempted to lower its prices by conservative placement of technology and tertiary services. In some environments in the United States this has resulted in an increase in the redundancy of standard as well as extremely specialised programmes (for example, organ or bone marrow transplant).

Hospitals providing training for technicians or graduate medical education cannot compete with non-teaching hospitals on the basis of price.

Hospitals that provide training for interns and residents and other allied health professions have expenses that are extensive and make them non-competitive in a price selective market. Yet the next generation of professionals is a policy goal (quality and quantity). Left solely to price, good training positions and the collective work of clinical faculties would be jeopardised. The highest quality training may or may not correlate with service needs of the patients served. This has required continued reconciliation in the payment policy for hospitals.

Hospitals could attempt to avoid low compliance patients in order to maximise their efficiency and promote themselves to other patient groups within their region.

'Dumping' has become the pejorative term for the avoidance of the patient who, by virtue of behaviour, ethnic background and traditions, poverty or other factors, becomes a less efficient patient to serve. To

128

compete for a broader base of patients with convenience for the physicians coupled with higher reimbursement has led to the need to reconcile this type of behaviour in some hospital markets and within the rules and regulations of some payment programmes.

Capital requirements of the individual hospital may not be addressed within a payment-based competitive system.

Theoretically, the hospital offering the most services should have the most patients and the most capital available because of the scale of revenues that are produced. However, the practical steps in responding to the needs of a hospital's community has led some institutions into the dilemma of providing technology, facility improvement, or facility expansion that would put them at a disadvantage next to the cost (and price) profile of the less programme responsive hospital. This may not have severe implications in the short run, but may cause a perverse incentive not to provide for services which in the long run may cost the society more due to the missed clinical opportunities to reduce mortality, morbidity, or disability in the population that has been served. To the degree price may drive patients to the lower cost hospital, this type of incentive could influence capital budget decisions in ways not suitable to the public interest.

Biomedical research in the applied clinical setting may directly or indirectly add cost and inefficiencies that compromise hospitals' ability to compete.

Payer agencies have had to deal with reconciling biomedical research programme costs associated with length of stay, equipment, staff, and procedures and processes including informed consent that add to the complexity of hospitalisation, its cost and the amenities offered the patient. To ignore these enterprises is not in the public interest. To allow such programmes to any and all who apply would compromise the overall costs and perhaps the quality of biomedical research. In a system designed to offer price or patient flow as elements of competition, biomedical research, protocol selection and control becomes an issue to be reconciled.

A second class of care becomes a political and consumer issue where hospitals compete for patients.

Whether perceived or real, when hospitals compete for patients, and any type of association becomes involved, the spectre of a second class of care can evolve. The UK plan should be extremely sensitive to this because the issue often comes into play in the US when public hospital roles (particularly in the inner-cities) are discussed among the citizenry. Hospitals capable of applying for independent status or hospitals successful in attracting patients may leave the remaining hospital with citizens' protestations regarding its programmes and their quality.

TRANSITION: WHEN HOSPITAL GOVERNANCE, LEADERSHIP AND MANAGEMENT MUST COMPETE TO SERVE

1. The investment of resources is significant if a dynamic and qualified governance process for a hospital is to be implemented.

   University hospitals have made the transition to private voluntary status. Likewise, public hospitals have left departmental status within city and county government to become private voluntary hospitals. Their success or failure has come not only from the corporate infrastructure and clinical programmes they have built, but rather from the governance process itself. The financial management, quality assurance monitoring, planning and development and operations work of the hospital must be organised into a plan with goals and accountability.

2. Hospitals may propose to implement new types of corporate structure for their activities to focus activity in a business context and avoid rules and regulations of hospitals.

   Such activities as the provision of supplies, delivery systems for durable medical equipment, joint projects with physicians and new or transitional relationships with historical sponsors brought some hospitals to reorganise the corporate structure of their institutions. The most common format was to produce a configuration of corporations that sustained the advantages of American tax law for hospitals, while acknowledging that some activities were better organised into traditional for-profit companies organisationally tied to the hospital. In part, these changes in structure came hand in hand with the movement towards more competition. There were cost appropriations made in these structures that made programme activity sustainable while offering lower prices for the direct provision of care.

3. Like governance, the investment in the management of a hospital was significant for the transition to a competitive operating environment.

   What does a hospital need to compete with other hospitals for the interest of a payer agency or a cluster of physicians?

   President and chief executive officer: Prerogatives to track information, formulate initiatives and take action must be increased in a hospital that will thrive by reacting to competitive goals and

130

opportunities. Staff support for this executive must be more elaborate to bring alive the Board's committee process as suggested above. In addition, many administrative departments will be enlarged to carry out new work. Some comments suggestive of these changes are:

Finance: Financial departments must be transformed from simple accounting operations into analysis and action teams. Negotiations rather than administering appropriations will characterise their transition.

Strategic planning: The planning function will be transformed from a facilities development into an overall business and market assessment and action group.

Public relations and advertising: The millions of dollars spent by individual hospitals in the United States on advertising and marketing is to develop name recognition in every home near the hospital and its physicians.

Wallpaper and beauticians: The hospitals that compete for the patient's choice find ways to promote themselves directly to those patients with personal amenities.

4. Transactions between third party payers and the hospital also add considerable necessary investment to administrative costs.
     The relative proportion of the health expenditure spent on administrative costs in the hospital is also based on the elements of control sought by the payer. New accounting sophistication to deal with rules regarding 'appropriate costs' will lead to new levels of detail in cost reporting.

5. Pressure to lower price by payer agencies is usually coupled with additional initiatives on their part to control and monitor quality. This too adds to administrative costs.
     Most recently, American hospitals have come under increasing standardisation of quality assurance methods. Agencies that do medical chart reviews have been through several generations of development. There are voluntary standards organisations that actually look to see the amount spent on computers for exclusive use in monitoring and follow-up on quality issues.

THE PAYER AGENCY: WHAT CAN IT DO TO CREATE POSITIVE SUPPORT OF THE HEALTH DELIVERY SYSTEM?

In the mid-1960s, the Federal and federal state programmes for poor people and aged people began an evolving process of approaches by payer agencies.

1. Payers should support the qualified and dynamic governance and management of hospitals.

    Payer agencies could simply assume that the hospitals will develop the expertise for its Board, hire dynamic and effective managers, and that the corporate and administrative structure will develop of its own accord. Positive support is more likely to ensure success.

2. Keep the payment methodology stable.

    In the US over the last five years, the payment method changed each year. The Federal government instituted new cost finding guidelines, DRGs and IPROs and mandatory quality assurance and site surveys.

    New developments, staff initiatives, new concepts for units of service or incentives will create a never-ending list of innovations to be implemented within the payment system. This development is reputable and necessary, but if it comes so fast and with such fundamental changes that hospital expertise is spent learning the new rather than planning and developing ways to thrive under the system, then the speed of change in the methodology itself becomes part of the problem in hospital management effectiveness.

3. The philosophy and policy of a payer agency ought to encourage individual and regional approaches.

    Regions or individual hospitals can sometimes develop novel approaches to the regionalisation of services, the sharing of risk for community health service use, the structure and management of hospitals or other approaches that are significant, but not necessarily applicable to other regions or institutions.

4. Hospitals, experts, and other interested parties should participate in an organised forum to advise the payer agency on reimbursement policy.

    The technical issues that have profound public policy implications (capital access, access for the poor, graduate medical education, biomedical research, technology access, programme development, and so on) will need to be discussed openly and understandably for all parties involved.

CONCLUSIONS

The recent regulatory, reimbursement, corporate restructure, quality assurance and competition history of the American hospital industry should be understood against the history and development of third-party payer methods not only to pay for services, but also to promulgate public policy through payment methods. Left alone, there was much to lose in the values and goals for health services within unbridled competition. At the same time, there were too many variables to allow a simple characterisation of that competition. There would be a necessary transformation of practice and talent within hospitals that are subjected to competition. Finally, if the payer function itself would become pro-active in fostering hospital management and governance and adaptive to new ideas, it too could become a meaningful public policy tool as well as the agency of the support for health services.(*)

Back to games
(Editor)

It is worth briefly pausing in this attempt to illuminate co-operation and friendliness by looking at a simple and well-known model. It has its roots in psychology and the analysis of transactions and interactions with individuals and groups. Many people know it, but few understand how to make it work for them.

The concepts are simple – winning and losing. If we return to my earlier discussion of traditional games, they are important where one individual or group is trying to win – or at least not to lose. Here, winning is good and losing is bad and it is fine to be the winner – though it is encouraged that we should be sporting with our losing opponents!

When these notions are placed in organisations, relationships or any kind or families the results are interesting. There are two important themes.

(*) The author acknowledges the significant contribution of Mr David R Ott, vice president and executive director of The Brooklyn Hospital Foundation, in the development of this paper.

1. *It is usually the wrong model. Most difficult things in society require everyone to win and there must be a recognition that this is both possible and desirable, and not hopeless. Policy-makers should struggle with all possible scenarios and packages until they find one which is as close to a win for everyone as possible (*).*

2. *Winners and losers behave and feel differently. The traditional game model means that if you lose once against someone, not only do you want to ensure that you don't lose again, but you may want, in some way or another, to 'settle the score'. This leads within organisations to some issues receiving disproportionate attention where they provide an arena for the 'second game' to be played. Managerial energy and time is then dissipated. It is not nice to have losers around; they are depressing and if they lose often enough can move into the mode of making sure that if they haven't won, neither will anybody else.*

   All this is neatly summarised in four positions (though this itself is over-simplified since there will frequently be more than two players).

1. *Lose-lose – war. Hopefully, we are beginning to see that no-one ever wins a war, however justified it may have been.*

2. and 3. *Win lose-lose win – an outcome which can leave most people, even the winners, feeling uncomfortable and watching their backs.*

4. *Win-win – the key place to be positioned in life, and where most interpersonal skills training is focused. Rick Norling's paper, once again against a background of the changing United States' system, looks at how the use of 'win-win' within a transition enabled successful outcomes. From the background of the 1992 United Kingdom, and topical debate about potential closures of old and famous London teaching hospitals, the notions contained within this paper may be particularly relevant. However, aspects of this paper suggest movement towards the old British publicly-funded approaches, with payers and providers in close relationship – an interesting counterpart to earlier British eztracts.*

(*) **Perceptive philosophers will see here traces of John Stuart Mill and utilitarianism.**

AN EXAMPLE OF A WIN-WIN STRATEGY IN MINNEAPOLIS

RICK NORLING (UNITED STATES)

INTRODUCTION

In the early 1980s both payers and health care providers in the United States began to recognise the power payers had to impact the way in which health care is delivered. This realisation of the interlocking nature of the provision and financing of health care resulted in a wide variety of organisational relationships between health care providers and payers. Typical responses on both sides were adversarial. In some cases, payers or providers even went as far as to venture into the other's business to gain control. There are, however, excellent long-standing models of integrated health care financing and delivery systems in the United States including the Kaiser-Permanente Health Systems. The payers and provider relationships spawned in the 1980s will need to pass the test of time to see if they are effective.

Fairview (of which I am chief executive officer) and Group Health Inc. (GHI) have, over the past twenty years, developed a relationship which has provided a winning situation for both organisations, and ultimately, the patients both organisations serve. This relationship is an example of how top managers within health care and payer organisations can develop lasting, mutually beneficial organisational outcomes. This paper will describe the relationship between Fairview and GHI, their grounding in a mutual not-for-profit philosophy and the evolution of the contractual relationship between the two organisations. The paper will go on to describe the current status of the relationship and the opportunities that are emerging for the two organisations, including the joint development of a health care service continuum and integrated quality standards as well as opportunities to broaden health care access to underserved populations. Finally, the paper will describe issues that Fairview and GHI must resolve in order to meet the environmental demands of the future. Both organisations must finally address the fundamental paradigm shift in the environment, which demands that health care organisations move from treating illness to improving the health status of populations.

Although much has been made of the competitive model within the

United States health care community during the past decade, discussion of future success through co-operation is re-emerging in the health care literature. Co-operation is viewed as a mechanism for compatible health care organisations to build integrated health care service continuums, which will allow them to compete more effectively. The relationship between Fairview and GHI serves as an excellent example of how two organisations, through co-operation rather than competition, can mutually ensure organisational success, while working toward impacting on the health needs of the community positively.

FAIRVIEW/GROUP HEALTH HISTORY

The relationship of Fairview and GHI dates from the late 1960s; however, the foundations of the relationship are grounded in each organisation's history.

Group Health Plan, a not-for-profit organisation with a consumer Board, was established during the mid-1950s. By the mid-1960s, Group Health had a medical staff of only seven (four full-time and three part-time physicians), but it had begun to grow. Although Group Health physicians practised at seven Twin Cities hospitals by this time, they were generally considered outcasts for what was then thought to be a radical group practice affiliation.

Fairview similarly had begun to grow by the mid-1960s. Founded in 1906, as a not-for-profit hospital, Fairview had outgrown its original location and begun to expand its hospital operations to a suburban site. There, Fairview began to evolve into a multi-hospital system with a corporate office, and the Fairview Riverside Hospital and the Fairview Southdale Hospital campus. When Fairview Southdale opened, many of Fairview Riverside's physicians chose to move their practices to the new site. It was determined that the addition of Group Health physicians to Fairview Riverside's medical staff would be an excellent way to replace migrating medical staff and bring substitute volume to Fairview Riverside.

Carl Platou, Fairview chief executive officer, approached Maurice McKay, general director of Group Health, about such a move during a dinner meeting in which they discussed the advantages of consolidating Group Health's hospitalisations at Fairview Riverside, to include a discount similar to that which Fairview offered Blue Cross/Blue Shield and to identify ways in which Group Health physicians might become more involved in Fairview Riverside's medical staff committee structure. An agreement between Group Health and Fairview was struck that evening and written on a napkin!

What began with that napkin agreement has developed into a strong

136

twenty year relationship with the advantages, costs, negotiation and compromise associated with a long-term commitment. The 'gentlemen's agreement' worked out over dinner and sealed with a handshake would not have grown had there not also been an affinity between the two organisations' philosophies and cultures. Both organisations believed in deliberate planning and careful use of resources. Group Health was dedicated to a not-for-profit, community board philosophy, as was Fairview. Group Health saw advantage in the consolidation of their hospitalisations for negotiating leverage and discount rates, and Fairview saw advantage in bolstering the even then sagging admissions of an inner-city hospital.

In particular, there was a need for a solid merger of the fee for service and Group Health physicians, since many private physicians still harboured a dislike for Group Health's philosophy. One physician on Fairview Riverside's medical staff who was familiar with several Group Health physicians, and respected them, acted as their champion, and their active participation on medical staff committees ultimately dissolved the barriers between the two groups.

During the mid-1980s, Group Health decided that it would develop a specialty clinic which would bring Group Health specialists to one location. Group Health solicited and received proposals from several organisations including Fairview Riverside. One local hospital in particular, Metropolitan Medical Center, made Group Health an extremely attractive offer. History, philosophy, pricing and the difficulty of relocating a medical staff of 240 all played a part in the decision of where to build the new specialty centre. Fairview saw the advantage of the continued relationship with Group Health's growing practice and the incremental volume that such a clinic would bring to Riverside Medical Center. Ultimately, a long range perspective prevailed in spite of better short-term pricing elsewhere, and Group Health decided to locate a new four-storey, 108,000 square foot primary care and specialty clinic which will increase Group Health's capacity to treat primary care patients by 50 per cent at the Fairview Riverside campus.

Even within this relatively conflict-free relationship, there were problems and opportunity costs for both organisations. Group Health was consistently pressured by its marketing department to expand its hospital network. Fairview recognised this as a threat, but was restricted in developing other long-term relationships with the growing managed care (HMO/PPO) marketplace at Fairview Riverside as a counter-balance to its strong Group Health affiliation. Group Health's business philosophy constantly required it to conduct analysis of whether to make or buy a given service. Although always an issue, it became a more crucial concern as other hospitals were put up for sale in the Minneapolis-St. Paul area. Not only could Group Health withdraw a particular ancillary procedure or test, it could have simply acquired its own hospital, leaving Fairview Riverside in a severe financial crunch.

During the 1980s, that make-buy analysis applied to physicians as well as ancillary services. As Group Health's growth allowed it to bring more and more specialty services into its structure, there were some occasions in which the physician who joined Group Health was unwilling to move his or her practice to Fairview Riverside from another hospital. In the case of a new urology specialist, patients who could be very adequately cared for at Fairview Riverside were no longer hospitalised at Fairview Riverside, but sent to Abbott Northwestern, a competing downtown hospital, due to physician preference. Overnight, Fairview Riverside lost almost 300 admissions and procedures per year.

Still the advantages of the relationship outweighed the disadvantages for both sides. Group Health continued to receive excellent contract rates. With the increasing size of the Plan and the number of physicians at Fairview Riverside, their negotiating clout grew. The fact that Fairview Riverside actively pursued and sought to develop a private medical staff whose patients were frequently insured by more favourable contracts, actually benefited Group Health by allowing their business to be priced on the margin. Group Health physicians were intimately involved in the medical staff hierarchy and programme design, and Fairview Riverside continued to benefit from the Group Health volume.

Fairview received the benefit of a long-term contract, working capital and guaranteed volumes to an inner-city hospital that was all but unheard of in the private sector. To Fairview's advantage, the leverage that Group Health had in negotiations was tempered with the good sense that understood the importance of keeping Fairview Riverside a financially healthy organisation. In addition, the volume that Group Health could be counted on to deliver acted as a base for the acquisition and development of specialty services, technology and equipment that might have not been otherwise possible or possible as quickly. Finally, the constant re-evaluation of service provision by Group Health resulted in a creativity in programme development and efficiency at Fairview Riverside that might otherwise have been slower to develop without the constant Group Health programme analysis.

To the patient's advantage, the close working relationship and familiarity of patient systems between Group Health and Fairview Riverside, both in the hospital and the emergency room, smoothed patient flow for a better patient experience. Physician participation in the medical staff committee structure assured consistent quality. The relationship encouraged innovation, which ultimately benefited the patient through new more efficient and effective services. Finally, the contracting

138

relationship between Group Health and Fairview Riverside broadened into a relationship with Fairview, which encompassed Fairview Southdale and Fairview Ridges Hospitals, in addition to Fairview Riverside.

During the late 1980s, the management of Fairview Riverside and St Mary's Hospital, which were adjacent and interconnected, saw an advantage in merging the two hospitals. Fairview and Carondelet LifeCare formed a joint venture company to combine and integrate the two hospitals, which was named Riverside Medical Center (RMC). Group Health physicians were familiar with St Mary's Hospital and the medical staff, but actually balancing the merger of the two organisations with the Fairview-Group Health relationship was a delicate one for Fairview.

CURRENT STATUS

Both Fairview and GHI have undertaken strategic planning processes recently and continue to find major areas of convergence. Key environmental issues that impact both organisations include: increasing health care costs, physician shortages, the quality of services, access to care and the tax-status of not-for-profit organisations. Taken together these changes mandate a fundamental paradigm shift for health care organisations, which will ultimately move health care providers through today's cost-driven solutions to the assumption of the responsibility for the total health care for a regional population.

Health care costs

Health care costs currently are at 11 per cent of the GNP and are estimated to grow to 15–16 per cent of the GNP in the year 2000. Thus far, the Government has been able to control hospital (Medicare A) payment levels to a 9 per cent annual increase. Medicare 'Part B' or the outpatient/physician component of Medicare has been growing at a 12–15 per cent rate over the past several years. It is anticipated that the implementation of the resource-based relative-value scale, will maintain a 9.9 per cent growth rate for Medicare outpatient and physician costs. The difference between the traditionally lower paying governmental health care programmes and the overall growth of health care costs has, over time, been shifted to employers, who are experiencing health insurance cost increases in the 15–20 per cent ranges. In Minnesota price increases for health plans have paralleled national increases over the past several years. Employers say that they can no longer sustain such large increases and remain financially viable, and are moving their business to HMOs and PPOs as a way to help manage costs.

139

Physician shortages

Health care organisations are also facing much greater competition for personnel, particularly primary care physicians. There is a shortage of primary care physicians throughout the United States. The AMAs Center for Health Policy Research estimates that the overall number of physicians is projected to grow 12.9 per cent by the year 2000, while the general/family practice specialty is projected as growing only 5.2 per cent. In addition to the low growth rate of general/family practitioners, demand for their services will increase, particularly in states such as Minnesota where 'managed care' programmes are common. There are a variety of potential reasons for this shortage of primary care physicians. Historically, graduate medical training programmes have been more focused on specialties and sub-specialisation, and have encouraged residents into greater rather than lesser specialisation. Also, physician incomes have traditionally increased with their level of specialisation. During the period 1977 to 1987, the median real net income for physicians in general increased at a rate of 0.5 per cent per year, while family practitioner's incomes declined 0.8 per cent annually. Minnesota is further handicapped in recruiting new family practitioners by lower than average income and reimbursement levels, due in part to higher levels of managed care penetration and lower Medicare regional payment differences.

Quality

Purchasers have also begun to question the quality of the services that they are receiving. Although no-one is precisely sure of the actual indicators that should be used to define quality, purchasers are beginning to demand evidence that the quality of the services provided by an organisation is adequate. Nationally, the federal government has allocated $US600 million to study quality outcomes over the next five years, while in Minnesota there are ongoing efforts to develop statewide clinical quality protocols for selected high volume procedures as a way to substantiate clinical quality.

Access

There is a growing debate on both the national and local level about the ability of those without health care insurance to access health care. Concerns about access to health care are also fuelling national debate about national health insurance. Within Minnesota during the 1988-1989 legislative session, 'Healthspan' legislation was proposed which would provide basic health care coverage to all Minnesotans. Although the Bill

140

did not make it successfully through the legislature, the debate resulted in further study by the Minnesota Healthcare Access Commission.

Tax-exempt status

Intertwined with access issues is another discussion which relates to the tax status of not-for-profit health care organisations, and the need for them to demonstrate their value to the community in order to continue to enjoy certain tax exemptions. Challenges to health care organisations' tax-exempt status have been levelled in Utah in particular, but also in a variety of other states, including Minnesota. The basic premise is that the health care industry is far enough removed from its charitable beginnings so as to no longer merit the special tax exemptions given to not-for-profit organisations. In the Utah case, the court held that providing a community benefit was not enough to justify tax-exempt status, but that organisations must 'gift' the community. Although most challenges have focused on levels of charity/community care, there is growing sentiment that health care organisations must also positively impact the health status of the community.

FAIRVIEW AND GROUP HEALTH'S FUTURE

Fairview's future

Fairview has recently gone through an extensive strategic planning process in which it has determined that the key to survival in the future will be its ability to make a paradigm shift from providing services to accepting accountability for the health status and delivery costs of a population. To do this Fairview recognises that it must manage costs and quality, while expanding the horizons of the 'hospital' perspective to include the full continuum of health care services. Treatment of the acutely ill is but one component of the continuum. Wellness must be maintained and when it cannot be, both ambulatory and hospital care must be provided for both the acutely and chronically ill. This continuum is not necessarily composed of Fairview services alone but can be accomplished within a network partnership. A variety of partners is needed to build such a continuum. However, among those providers, physicians are key. The continuum of services must be built to meet the needs of the patients, payers and purchasers. Ultimately, the greater a payer or purchaser such as Group Health is involved in the process of continuum development, the greater the benefit to both organisations and patients through integration of care.

The mechanisms that integrate a network, such as quality outcome indicators and information systems, are another key in the development and maintenance of Fairview's network. Although always committed to quality, it is not until recently that the community and major providers have asked Fairview and other health care providers for proof of that quality. The development of demonstrable indicators of both service and clinical quality are considered a key part of Fairview's future. Fairview must also ensure the level of quality throughout its network by working with network partners to meet appropriate quality criteria. The ability to share and transfer data quickly throughout the network is a key to its ultimate ability to function effectively. Fairview and Group Health have begun discussions in how they can work together to develop and implement quality improvement programmes.

Fairview believes that it must use its network to provide care to those who do not have access to resources, as well as those who do. Providing charity/community care and what has been called within Fairview 'community dividending', or providing socially significant but unprofitable programmes such as a battered woman's programme, will remain an important Fairview commitment to the community to expand access to health care. Fairview must also clearly communicate its commitment to charity/community care so as to address concerns that are arising regarding the appropriate tax status of all not-for-profit organisations.

It is crucial to understand the definitions of three basic elements of the health care environment: payers, purchasers and sponsors. Payers are those organisations that provide the technical service of paying the provider. Payers may or may not assume risk. Purchasers, alternatively, provide the financing for the health care of a population. Finally, sponsors assure that the individual's needs are met in an equitable fashion. Each of these are distinct roles in the financing and organisation of health care, which could be assumed by a single entity.

Group Health's future

Group Health has been as affected by these national trends as has Fairview. Group Health has grown from 4,300 members and one physician in 1960 to 264,500 members and 240 physicians in 1989. Its staff model HMO (*) design has shown a consistent ability to control cost and fee increases better than other 'looser' managed care designs such as PPOs. A

(*) A Health Maintenance Organisation directly employing physicians and until recently very unusual in the United States, but growing.

combination of complete coverage and price leadership has resulted in employers' demand for Group Health coverage that has outstripped its ability to provide services.

In addition to its own growing business in Minnesota, Group Health must also address the needs of both the Government, through Medicare HMO and Social-HMO (SHMO) projects, and national employer accounts. It currently acts as the local representative for several national organisations, the HMO Group, Kaiser-Permanente Health Systems and Prudential Insurance. These groups not only demand Group Health's expansion in terms of its ability to serve HMO members, but also to expand its products beyond its HMO tradition into PPOs and non-acute health care products.

Group Health is nonetheless faced with restricting its growth to a level to which it can continue to deliver quality services, if it is unable to expand its provider base. Group Health, therefore, needs to continue to expand its services and adopt more medical staff, particularly primary care physicians. This need is unfortunately complicated by the national shortage of primary care physicians, described earlier. This has led Group Health to consider the concept of affiliating with other organisations such as the Ebenezer Society in the case of their SHMO demonstration project or other physician clinics. The Ebenezer Society, for example, augments Group Health's abilities in the areas of long-term care, home care, social services, transportation and case management across a broad spectrum of services. As these relationships grow Group Health must address quality and information transfer questions similar to those facing Fairview.

Another key issue for all not-for-profit health care organisations in the United States is the current discussion of tax status. Group Health, as a not-for-profit managed health plan, faces issues similar to Fairview in this area, and must, like Fairview, continue to develop mechanisms to demonstrably return value to the community at large.

Fairview and Group Health see several areas of convergence in network development, mutually expanding each others' capacity and service areas, providing expanded access to care and positively impacting the health care of the community. In addition, Fairview and Group Health have the ability to develop compatible systems, which will aid each organisation in clinical quality and information management throughout their 'mini-system' and thus improve patient care. Jointly developing a service continuum and associated case management protocols would also place Fairview, Group Health and their network partners in the position of being able to service the health care needs of a population, and to assume risk for a regional population, if necessary.

EMERGING OPPORTUNITIES

Fairview/Group health network development

In response to the issues of increasing health care costs and demand for managed care services, Fairview and Group Health have begun to look at the development of networks for specific projects. Fairview has been committed over the years to the development of a group of strong primary care physicians who are affiliated with its hospitals. It views those physicians as the core of the network it believes as being so essential to future models of health care provision. Group Health is faced with the need to expand its clinical capacity and broaden its physician group to deliver an expanded product line (that is, PPOs) to its national accounts. Fairview and Group Health have discussed the opportunity jointly to build a primary and specialty care network, utilising Fairview affiliated physicians and selected other partners, such as the Ebenezer Society. This network would immediately meet Group Health's needs to expand their capacity and could be used as the basic network to service a PPO product. For Fairview there would be several advantages to such an arrangement beyond the obvious increased volume to Fairview facilities. As Group Health continues to market its products, Fairview would encourage them to expand into areas in which Fairview currently has low or no penetration thus expanding Fairview's geographic market penetration and market share, both strategic goals. As Group Health develops relationships with employers, Fairview could work with Group Health to target specific employers Fairview wishes to develop relationships with, again a key strategy. Setting up such a network builds working relationships and continues to expand the experience of Group Health, Fairview and the other partners with a shared approach to providing comprehensive services. Finally, Fairview would continue to build network relationships with other providers in the community which meets its needs for network development and geographic coverage throughout the Twin Cities.

Integrating mechanisms development

Both Fairview and Group Health are anticipating environmental demands for information and quality systems that far out-pace the types of systems that are in place today. Both organisations have embarked on major efforts to expand and upgrade their current MIS systems. Clearly there is an opportunity to develop compatible systems and to work toward a paperless transfer of patient financial, clinical, demographic and quality information. Of particular interest is the development of quality systems. Each

144

organisation has quality indicators, but they would need to be integrated. Finally the network must be co-ordinated in some manner to guarantee continuity and quality.

Issues that surround this discussion are the basic compatibility and functionality of various types of information systems. Issues regarding the types of information to be shared and confidentiality of such information are key, particularly as the discussion moves to quality indicators.

Commitment to unserved populations

Fairview and Group Health have also had discussions regarding the intertwined issues of the mission of not-for-profit organisations, their commitment to the community and the growing trend among local and state governments to withdraw tax exemptions from those organisations that do not live up to their community commitments. These discussions have lead Fairview and Group Health to the joint development of a charity care programme. This programme is currently in its final design stages.

Developing these 'emerging opportunities' together, Fairview and Group Health begin to move beyond their historical contracting relationship, in which the Fairview Riverside or now the Riverside Medical Center-Group Health connection dominated, into an era in which the organisational relationship between the Fairview system and Group Health takes precedence. Further expansion and definition of that relationship will enable Fairview and Group Health to develop the shared future vision that will ultimately become necessary for both organisations to flourish in the future.

SHARED FUTURE VISION

Fairview and Group Health have recently committed to sharing their strategic plans and developing a shared future vision. It is believed that these actions will move their relationship beyond contracts and cost emphasis to one that focuses on the assumption of responsibility for the health care of a regional population. In a sense the challenges that face Fairview and Group Health, as that process evolves, are a microcosm of the larger issues facing both public and private health care providers in other regions.

Three key issues that will emerge as this relationship evolves relate to:

- how the network will be expanded and integrated

- how the network will be financed

- how the network will impact the health status of a population.

1. *Expanded network development*
   As health care provider experience with the network concept grows, and purchaser demand for health care network products increase, it would seem more effective to develop a consistent set of network providers who are joined together in a stronger, more defined relationship. Moving toward that stronger network raises issues that extend beyond those raised in the development of project specific networks. The issue of who are network partners remains, however. Added to that are concerns about the type (that is, joint marketing and risk sharing) and exclusivity of the commitment that will be asked of each partner.

Physicians remain a key part of the development of the network. From Fairview's viewpoint it must consider how it would manage its full medical staff if only certain physicians are selected to participate in the network. Given the shortage of primary care physicians, the pressure on Group Health to grow, and given Group Health's structure, which relies heavily on primary care physicians and uses Group Health specialists rather than outside referral physicians, Group Health may wish to admit only primary care physicians into the network.

Integrating mechanisms

Integrating mechanisms become even more important as the network expands to include groups that complete a geographic network for acute and non-acute services including nursing homes, home care agencies and various support service organisations. Consideration must be given to internal policies and procedures, quality standards, information needs and level of care transition processing needs. Business practices must be re-examined to allow for the successful development of the partnership. As the network expands, is the administration and co-ordination of the network best left with the individual organisations, or must each sacrifice some autonomy to an umbrella organisation? Is a regional network appropriate for providers, but inadequate for a payer, who must contract with national employers?

146

Commitment to unserved populations

The network must also develop a consistent policy toward the underserved, provided on an individual or network basis. Network partners could redefine their commitments to the community in terms that are more relevant for a network than an individual care provider. Would the network provision to the underserved be able to honour the spirit of each individual organisations commitment to the community? How much financial risk could/should be absorbed by the participants?

2. *Financing the regional network*
    Once the means are in place to deliver health care with an effective provider network that can service a region which has a strong relationship with a payer, then it is possible to access a population and positively affect its health status. This requires issues of cost control, organisation change, acute orientation and much else to be addressed.

3. *Impacting the health status of a regional population*
    With both provider network and financing mechanisms in place, the network can begin to have a significant impact on the health status of a population. How are those improvements defined and measured? Certainly there are standard public health measurements which can be used to evaluate a population's health status, but do those indicators adequately reflect today's health care concerns? On a macro basis, are there social issues such as teenage pregnancy, drug usage or abuse that must be considered in the measurement of health status? Is not only the status of the individual important, but also the service quality of their treatment significant? If so, how do we define and subsequently measure those indicators? Are chronic problems adequately addressed by a network in which many partners have an acute care bias? Finally, if the network is able to define these issues, how will they be appropriately measured?

Such questions are enormous and begin to get to the heart of the issues facing not only Fairview and Group Health as they move into the future, but also other organisations in other regions in the United States. These questions are similar to those facing other nations as well.

CONCLUSION

This paper began by describing Fairview and Group Health's historical relationship and how it has been used effectively by both organisations. The paper described some of the current opportunities that are being presented by the environment, and ways that Fairview and Group Health can capitalise on them to their mutual benefit and the benefit of the patients they serve. Finally, the paper posed questions that both organisations must face as they move forward to meet the challenges of the next decade. The answers to those questions will provide input to Fairview and Group Health's development, but may also prove useful to other regions in the United States as well.

The key to success in the future will be to face the fundamental changes in health care being presented by the environment and to manage organisational relationships through those transitions. The challenges faced by Fairview and Group Health in moving from their historical contractual relationship to one which jointly responds to the emerging health care environment are by necessity grounded in the United States system and economy. The broader issues raised through this relationship, however, can serve as a focus for other areas of the United States and as a basis of discussion for other countries. Alternatively, the experience of others can be enormously helpful as Fairview and Group Health work out those solutions in their micro environment.

The New South Wales Doctors' Dispute (Editor)

Diane Horvath's paper looks at a dispute that initially involved doctors and then spilled into nursing. It illustrates how the inability to work in a 'friendly' fashion can reduce the effectiveness of any organisation, and lay down seeds of mistrust and antagonism for the future. It highlights the fragile nature of complex organisational relationships and the need for goodwill to be consciously worked towards at all times, irrespective of the immediate issues in hand. If 'win-win' cannot be the outcome, then it is only the brave and extremely well organised who can work towards 'win-lose' and be certain a) that it won't be 'lose-lose' and b) that it will be they who win and not the others.

It is highly relevant in the overall context of provider dominance of which doctors are a part. Any reduction in perceived power tends to be resisted and, therefore, requires even greater skill to ensure a good outcome.

148

HOW DO THE DIFFERENT PLAYERS DEAL WITH THE CHANGING DEMANDS OF THE OTHERS?

DIANE HORVATH (AUSTRALIA)

Australia has a long history of disputes between medical professions and the Government in relation to the provision of health services and their funding. The underlying fears of 'nationalised medicine', and the equating of 'fee-for-service' private medicine with professional autonomy, have even led to a Special Constitutional Amendment and to a series of struggles over Government funding of National Health Insurance in the 1970s and 1980s – Medibank and Medicine.

In the late 1970s and early 1980s, New South Wales' hospital budgets were being reined in, and the then minister for health Laurie Brereton closed a number of long-standing inner-city hospitals and attacked doctors on a number of fronts – accusing them of overservicing and coercing patients to be treated as 'private'. The situation in New South Wales was, therefore, explosive.

When Medicare was being implemented, the Policy Committee was mindful of the mistake made in 1974 when salaried radiologists and pathologists left public hospitals because they were denied rights of private practice. In providing for this, the Policy Committee wanted to exercise some level of control – thus was conceived the infamous 'Section 17' of The National Health Insurance Act. This section gave the Federal health minister the power to determine the form of contract between doctors and hospitals in relation to their private practice rights, and carried no mechanism for appeal. It was passed by Federal Parliament in September 1983. Negotiations between Federal and State government had resulted in guidelines for contracts which included 'capped' medical charges for private patients in public hospitals, and hospital facility charges on doctors.

The Federal AMA was pressuring Government about Section 17, and in 1985 an Inquiry was established into private practice in hospitals, chaired by Professor Penington (then Dean of Medicine in Melbourne, Victoria). Pending its deliberations, Section 17 contracts were deferred.

In New South Wales, Laurie Brereton gazetted Regulation 54A of the

149

Public Hospitals Act, giving it power to regulate maximum private medical fees charged in public hospitals. At this stage, a group of 'rebel surgeons' in New South Wales rejected the Inquiry (which the AMA was participating in) and threatened to strike. Federally, the AMA was achieving compromises and agreements, but in New South Wales the orthopaedic surgeons finally resolved to resign their public hospital appointments. They saw government actions to date as 'the thin end of the wedge' for nationalised medicine, and established a theory of conspiracy between State and Federal Labor governments aimed at limiting doctors' private practice rights. In the hostile and suspicious environment of New South Wales this theory was readily accepted.

Once again, however, there had been a lot of activity in New South Wales, where Laurie Brereton had enacted Section 42 of the New South Wales Public Hospitals Act. This Section 42 gave the Government power to regulate the terms of appointment of visiting practitioners to public hospitals, and covered their conduct not only in public hospitals, but elsewhere. It was couched in somewhat provocative language, and aimed at preventing doctors from applying coercion to their patients.

In the middle months of 1984, resignations of visiting practitioners started to come in. A new health minister had succeeded Laurie Brereton – a far more conciliatory individual who would probably have contrived to make some form of peace with the State. However, the whole situation was very much in the news, and the Labor party state conference and premier decided to recall parliament and pass special legislation to render all resignations within certain dates inoperative, and to ban for seven years any doctor who resigned thereafter.

The effect was electric! Never before or since have I seen the whole profession so united. The issue became one of solidarity. The conspiracy theory was proved overnight. The AMA called on all doctors to withdraw services (other than emergency care) from all public hospitals. Resignations poured in, and while waiting for them to take effect, services were withdrawn.

A militant, well organised and publicity-seeking group of surgeons (now calling themselves 'Procedural Specialists') fanned the flames. Every grievance since Federation was trotted out. Waverers were 'persuaded' into compliance.

With respect to hospital services, a significant number of big district hospitals were totally without orthopaedic surgical services, or had a sole practitioner left. Many such hospitals stood on the major highways in and out of Sydney. As road accident victims were brought to these Casualties, a search would begin for a place to send them where care could be provided. Quickly, the general public learnt to bypass many of the district and community hospitals and come directly to the teaching hospitals.

Elective admissions were cancelled wholesale, and eye surgery, for example, became almost unknown. Reacting to this, many surgeons began to set up in the private hospitals. Until then, New South Wales had a large public sector – composed largely of small <50 bed hospitals with limited capability. The vast majority of private patients were treated in the public hospitals where a more sophisticated level of service was supplied.

As the dispute continued, whole specialties set up in private hospitals as a means of survival – and private hospital proprietors welcomed them with open arms. Others expanded their office procedures and began looking to establish day surgery centres. All became increasingly aware of their vulnerability if government owned the places where they earned their living.

Meanwhile a State Negotiating Committee was established, which haggled over offers and counter-offers on a very long list of claims – including private hospital legislation, and the right of the profession to be consulted about any hospital policies, and to have a contract that could not be changed by future legislation!

In June 1984, the Penington Progress Report was released – a magnificent document which pointed wisely towards future directions. He played a crucial role in mediation by listening to the complete litany of concerns by all parties, and thoughtfully analysing their bases.

After considerable behind-the-scenes negotiations, the special Negotiating Committee of doctors (not the AMA) submitted a long list of claims to the State Government. The Commonwealth health minister and Federal AMA president then sent a joint letter to all doctors in Australia inviting review of the Penington Progress Report. Agreement was reached between New South Wales State Government and New South Wales Health. AMA was recommending a return to work in public hospitals. By this stage, however, the profession had split once again, with one segment constantly changing and increasing its range of demands; the other getting back to work.

Once again the dispute flared up on remuneration packages, until the New South Wales Government offered an interim increase while resolving the issue of whether a costly arbitration case would be brought. The AMA rejected this and the strike resumed in many hospitals (although not the teaching hospitals). A temporary truce was declared over Christmas, and representatives of the profession met with the prime minister to discuss the viability of private practice in public hospitals. As negotiations dragged on, the New South Wales Government started to recruit overseas to fill some critical vacancies, and the presidents of the learned Colleges called for a moratorium to permit proper negotiation. Finally, the Federal prime minister and state mremier met with the AMA and issued an unequivocal statement that medical practice would not be nationalised, and recognised

151

the importance of promoting private practice in public hospitals.

In April, 1985 a package was offered by State and Federal governments which included significant increases in doctor remuneration, repeal of unattractive legislation, and injection of significant capital monies for equipment, a change in health insurance policies, and deregulation of the private hospital industry. By early May these were accepted and the strike ended. In May, 1985 the Federal parliament passed the package of leglislation.

However, a strong faction had emerged within the AMA – led by the rebel surgeons. This faction has progressively ousted the pre-existing regime – first in New South Wales and then in May 1990 their leader became Federal president. The group has sought to change totally the image of negotiation by the profession – having been taught most effectively that a democratically elected government will accede to bullying and standover tactics where sweet reason will fail. This faction has billed itself as the 'Reform Group', and is dedicated to restoring the power and importance of the erstwhile 'honorary' specialist. A series of 'craft groups' have been established within the AMA – and it is most interesting to note that the Physician Craft Group (Internal Medicine) which is open to all F.R.A.C.P.s, only accords voting rights to those that are in full-time private practice – thus deliberately excluding the 40 per cent of physicians in hospital, salaried or academic positions.

During the period of the dispute, the role of patients was instructive. Despite considerable effort on the part of the New South Wales Government to locate and publicise the suffering of individual patients, very little emerged. The consumer movement failed to register any concerns, and the compliance and cheerfulness of patients who moved endlessly through the hospitals seeking (and frequently failing to obtain) timely care, was extraordinary. The community, as a whole, supported the doctors. It is difficult to know whether this is a reflection of the general Australian attitude that individuals fighting government are always worthy of support; or whether the power of individual doctors in relation to the sick is too personal to endanger.

A further issue for concern is the impact of the dispute on the nursing profession. At the time, there was already a shortage of nurses, associated with the increasing sophistication of hospital care and hence patient dependency, and exacerbated by the abrupt decision of the New South Wales Government to transfer nursing education into College training programmes and out of hospital apprenticeship-style training. The 'doctors' dispute' had its major impact in surgery – theatres stood idle, specialty surgical wards emptied, and then in the teaching hospitals they filled with emergency patients. The nurses, who had been trying to cope with their own identity crisis, now had to face the fact that doctors did not hold patient care sacred – that it was okay to desert patients if you were fighting government over matters of high moral principle like 'Should he who pays the piper call the tune?'. The doctors came back, but the nurses did not – they found their skills were very commercially attractive. The aspect that makes nursing different from most other service careers is the 'caring'. If this is removed as a proper goal, the competition of the marketplace becomes unbalanced. Nursing pay scales have now been renegotiated in New South Wales (and the rest of Australia) by as much as 30 per cent in real terms.

The most important impact has been on the social fabric of the collegiate system of medicine. The basic ethic of altruism has been shaken to its foundations. Individual members of the profession feel angry, hurt, resentful and suspicious of group activity unless it has an obvious and immediate personal reward. Even the sense of pride and participation in the Royal College is waning, let alone the belief in contribution to the public hospitals. Like most things, this is not a uniform set of absolutes, but rather a subtle shifting of the base of the pyramid, the whole spectrum moving across, to a stage where medicine is a career doctors advise their children not to pursue.

The antagonism between doctors as providers and government as payers continues to by dysfunctional, but the patients have yet to assert themselves as players on the field.

It is interesting to compare the situation, not altogether dissimilar, of the earlier crippling 'pilots' dispute'. Here the domestic airlines pilots imposed bans and then resigned 'en bloc' in support of a substantial pay claim. The Federal Government made use of airforce transport planes on commercial routes, and assisted the airline companies to recruit pilots overseas. The general public supported the government and the airline companies throughout, and put up with enormous inconvenience and delay in travel for nearly a year – always blaming the pilots for holding the country to ransom. The two constitute a fascinating comparison.

For hospital managers, it was a strange feeling – watching two armies fight a battle when the battlefield is the hospital you manage. Hospital managers were essentially spectators in relation to the main event, organising emergency services behind the scenes and negotiating with both armies, like worried farmers trying to sow and harvest their crops.

The clinicians distrust us mightily. We are perceived as an arm of government, afraid of losing our jobs, and with our boards fearful of dismissal. Their commitment to the corporate 'hospital' has dramatically fallen.

When I worked at John's Hopkin's in the early 1970s, we used a catch phrase – 'caring is part of the cure'. If we have another dispute, or even if we don't, who will feel committed enough to 'care'?

To win or lose, you have to play

(Editor)

As noted earlier, patients should always come first. However, it is usually much less clear how or where that is happening and how we recognise it. Anyone working in health care will remember issues where every possible aspect was canvassed, except that which immediately involved patients, whether individually or as a group.

John Morris describes how, in Australia, the confusion of roles between the federal and state governments, an obsession in recent years with issues about funding and the sharp competition among providers combined to create a situation in which people merely pay lip-service to the needs of patients. In a recent strengthening of consumer representation in the public hospitals of Victoria, he sees a small chink of light.

154

SO, WHO SPEAKS FOR THE PATIENT?

JOHN MORRIS (AUSTRALIA)

INTRODUCTION

The Australian health system has long had apparent separation of health care providers and those who pay for it.

Provision of health services has traditionally been the responsibility of State governments, in conjunction with the private sector. In colonial days, hospitals were generally established in the private sector and increasingly subsidised by governments. As government involvement increased, legislation regulating hospitals was introduced. Today 'public hospitals' reflect this mixed history providing care for private patients as well as for those without means. Truly private hospitals independent of government subsidy have also developed.

Funding of health services is primarily the responsibility of the Federal government, since from 1942 it has held all income tax powers and hence the bulk of revenue. Funding is both direct through a universal insurance system and indirect through grants to the States for the provision of hospitals, community health and other services. In addition, a number of private health funds (insurance companies) provide cover for hospitalisation.

Government involvement has invariably been introduced in the name of patient protection, either to ensure provision of kinds of care not satisfactorily provided through the private sector, to increase equity through the improvement of access for those with limited means, or through regulation to ensure standards are met or to promote efficiency.

Most providers (both hospitals and private practitioners) also lay claim to a history of advocacy for patient requirements. In particular, the charitable origins of the public hospitals and the history of governing boards representative of the community has led to a firmly held belief that they are mainly accountable to and act for the patient community.

However, in both the provision and funding of health services, the Australian system is characterised by divided responsibility and deficient linkages, which offer many incentives and opportunities for cost shifting and revenue maximisation by the public and private sector participants. Divisions, overlaps and uncertain boundaries exist between:

- the responsibilities of Federal and State governments;

- public and private sectors, with respect to both services, provision and funding; and

- provision and funding of services of different types, many of which are actual or potential substitutes for each other.

As a result, the increasing tension between payer and providers in Australia has been more related to the shedding of responsibility, or shifting of funding and patients between sectors or services types, than to the genuine interests of patients.

The traditional patient advocacy role of government is thus greatly weakened. The advocacy role of providers has been reduced both by the increased control exercised by government or insurers, and by the pressure to reduce costs.

LESSONS FOR AUSTRALIA

The uncertainty between the role of the Federal government and the State's has created an environment where either level of government can shift responsibility to the other, thus avoiding both the need for rational debate and public accountability for problems.

Lack of clarity between public and private providers and the different treatment of the two sectors in present funding arrangements, has created a two class hospital system and may preclude a more efficient source of resources.

Governments no longer need to act, and seem not to act, as effective advocates for the needs of patients. This is because of the ability in this confused system to avoid responsibility for service shortfalls and because of the pressure on governments to reduce overall expenditures.

Providers, either because of the difficulty of applying pressure on governments, or because in the present economic climate of the need to compete selfishly with others, have also lost much of their advocacy role. Recent experiences have shown that advocacy for the needs of patients seems absent or at least inadequate.

Relatively new patient advocacy groups such as the Consumer Health Forum, Health Issues Centre, and the Victorian District Health Councils, have not been obviously significant voices. However, a number of attempts to explain issues in political debates were published by the Health Issues Centre and the Consumer Health Forum has undertaken a study of health markets and insurance.

At the provider level, public hospitals in Victoria have been required to expand their relationships with consumer representatives and groups. Several hospitals have included consumer representation in their planning activities. These emerging relationships may assist in ensuring that even with ongoing uncertainty, patient needs and requirements gain greater consideration than they have in our recent past.

THE RESULT OF THE 'F' PLAN – THE STORY SO FAR

I shall not attempt a tidy conclusion to a book which, as noted at the beginning, is about managing untidiness, ambiguity and uncertainty.

As we move from this conference and its outcomes to the King's Fund's next contribution to important health debates, much is changing. The world economy appears locked in recession, the health needs of former Communist countries, ethnic minorities everywhere and Africa seem to overshadow old worries. The cliche of our 'global village' has new relevance.

The abiding message is, therefore, for all. Each of us in a position of authority and responsibility can choose between disempowerment or empowerment. Do we say, 'It's the system' or 'You can never change anything round here' or 'Be **** the system – together we can make it happen'.

The challenges and difficulties faced by health care systems throughout the world and the economies in which they are embedded will make that choice more stark. At the time of drafting this book, in 1991-92 in the United Kingdom, the changes in that health care system can be seen. The struggle and the different viewpoints are often defined as left and right. An alternative and more helpful viewpoint suggests that it is between old and new views of how organisations change. This contrast is distributed across the political spectrum. In addition, there is a personal dimension. It is possible to observe professionals, largely clinical, who by virtue of their personality and training are more happy with conventional approaches to organisation change. These are likely to include overt 'top down', so called rational, models of change, where the medical voice will be heard on appropriate committees and commissions arguing about what changes to make or to prevent. Alongside this traditional view can be seen a body, often labelled managers, who, also by virtue of temperament and, (sometimes), training take a different view of how organisations change. Where the professional fails to talk with the manager, the left winger with the right winger, the old with the young, there is liable to be a large degree of confusion and apparent acrimony as organisations seek to find new ways of coping with new challenges.

What seems important to me is that those of us working in the field of

159

health care delivery should be at the forefront of new management thinking – the cutting edge – rather than lagging behind and seeking to apply discredited and outmoded theories long after other sections of the economy have learned from their mistakes.

EMPOWERMENT – A RESULT OF THE 'F' PLAN

So far the 'F' plan has provided a loose framework for these papers. The conference found another for its discussion – and the final section of the book takes empowerment as its unifying concept.

The issue of 'beyond provider dominance' is not necessarily a replacement of the provider influence by something else within a zero sum. Providers may remain dominant, even in different circumstances – but the other parties may handle the situation differently, and take dominance themselves over aspects of health and health care.

It could be that the amount of power in the health system is finite. If so, then players have to compete for the available 'pie' and dislodge one another. However, it may not be so. We, arguably, can increase the power of the other players, and the total power in the system, without necessarily decreasing that of the providers.

In addition, it is interesting to have a more sophisticated view of providers – to see them as less monolithic or united. Each provider, institution or profession is itself a broad church – with many internal conflicts. How they resolve these and which 'group' dominates may be as important as issues between providers and others. Notions of empowerment often lead our thinking towards users or clients. Frequently in an enterprise as large and complex as a health care delivery system, issues about relative power are more indistinguishable and subtle.

Tensions abound as elsewhere between

guidance	and	delivery
professionals	and	Managers
one professional	and	another professional
payers	and	providers
providers	and	users

and many others.

If win-win is to be achievable then we must empower the weaker. If we try to disempower the stronger, we may end up with lose-lose – as suggested in some of the care studies in the earlier chapters.

The following paper looks specifically at empowerment. It also acts as a summary for the earlier themes of focus, speed, flexibility and friendliness – for these inevitably underlie the ability to act and feel powerful.

Community empowerment –
a result of the 'F' Plan
(Editor)

Throughout the book, various papers have referred to changing values, to moving from the health of an individual to the health of communities and of consulting and empowering users and clients. Without care, this can be simply rhetoric. As with any other form of organisational life, there has to be a place or an arena where power can be seen and used and where forms of trading can take place. Glen Garlick's paper, in the context of a relatively small New Zealand community, looks at the practicalities of inserting into the formal system a community health advisory group. As his paper demonstrates, it initially meant many things to many people, and he traces the tensions evident as the system as a whole learned to live with a new player and a new need to negotiate, listen and act.

COMMUNITY EMPOWERMENT: CREATING A DOMAIN OF POSITIVE CONFLICT

GLEN GARLICK (NEW ZEALAND)

INTRODUCTION

When existing power holders wish to empower others, it is essential to create a location for dialogue and consultation. In the context of our topic of 'beyond provider dominance', this will relate to moving power on to the axis representing users and payers. It may be an area where few relationships have existed before, or one where there has been a large imbalance, normally in favour of funding agencies.

Interestingly, a political desire to create greater empowerment and thus diffusion and confusion can run parallel with the desire for greater public accountability. Thus,the one force moves us towards delegation and the other towards centralisation – so the processes of dispersal and focus are operating simultaneously.

This paper is based on observations of a process in New Zealand, whereby Health Service Management Boards sought a method of creating consultation and empowerment through formal means. I have avoided specific New Zealand aspects, and sought to extract lessons and themes which will be relevant across all our health services as we move into a world of changing expectations and objectives for our systems.

It is worth noting that this process followed more than a decade of discussion about empowerment and involvement. Inevitably, this created high expectations – which are likely to be transferred onto any agency or group which emerges as a result. In addition, the very nature of the process is likely to be confusing and unco-ordinated, and this can lead to rapid frustration amongst people who carried those high expectations and may not understand the complexity of setting up new ways of doing things.

162

COMMUNITY HEALTH ADVISORY GROUPS – A CASE STUDY

The New Zealand solution was to set up Community Health Advisory Groups – (CHAGs). While this was a national endeavour with the hope of 20-25 of them being created over a fairly short timescale, it is inevitable in a country with large rural areas that community generated responses would be different. Their size also varied, ranging from 5-18 members. There was relatively little Government direction as to their powers and freedom and the formation process itself was managed in many different ways. This in itself is interesting – so for example:

- some existing groups became CHAGs after testing their local support
- some district councils became the local agent for the board in setting up the CHAGs
- some communities accepted nominations via the District Council with little public consultation
- in some areas carefully designed consultation processes were implemented by the area health board.

This naturally led to not only different size, membership and origin but also different styles of meetings. Some were 'committees' with minutes, procedures and all the paraphernalia of government agencies. Others were more informal but often met more frequently. Thus a national agency with a commonly agreed title became a wide range of quite differing bodies all seeking, at least in theory, to empower its local community and change the balance of power towards users and away from providers and funders.

OBSERVATIONS ON THE PROCESS

I have set out, in the following paragraphs, some of the key points that seem to me to emerge from this process.

True to their origins

Some CHAGs remain captive to their history. This is particularly noticeable in those which grew from 'a save our hospital' campaign – and there are other single issue groups which have managed to take over the CHAG. This has, fairly self evidently, led to a confusion between consultation in its widest and general sense and groups pre-programmed to work on specific objectives such as maintaining current services.

163

However, the most important potential takeover bid has come from the providers! This has worked through involving provider staff in the formation and staffing of community committees – and there is a concern that the provider influence is thus too strong. In the main, this has been less the provider self promoting and more the communities insisting that their local health professionals are the ones who can best represent them! It is a paradox within the area of power studies, that people often rush to return the power to those from whom it has been wrested.

Political skills

The level of political and negotiating skill varies greatly among CHAGs. Some groups are informal and loose in organisation while others are well organised, capable of marshalling public opinion and making strong public stands. The health board, seeking to receive advice through the CHAG channel, needs to be aware that there is little homogeneity in the advice or the process through which it was obtained.

Suspicion

Groups in various communities have typically been trying to obtain more say in health decision making for some years. Having been ignored, they now see a devious bureaucracy behind the current initiative and are thus suspicious. At a different level, members of the managing health boards feel that there may be little return from the CHAG effort – and notice that some of the group have well-known members who have long been a thorn in the side of the board.

Consultation/action

The level of power in the CHAG is still often exaggerated. It is widely observed internationally that the act of consultation is often taken as a signal that advice given will be acted upon. The initial views of CHAGs range from a threatening – 'if our advice isn't acted upon you can ...' to a much gentler – 'all we ask is that you hear our case and treat us fairly'.

Our model/your model

As with all consultative committees, knowledge about the main sponsoring organisation is not always great, and certainly varies. The health providers may see the CHAG as a major element allowing direct contact between the users of services and those paying for them. However, many members of

164

CHAGs see their roles as supervisors of standards, a watchdog on the board and a focus for issues and complaints from consumers. These confusions can be clarified over time, both as the process is worked on and as members of the CHAGs have better knowledge of complaints procedures.

EMERGENT PROPERTIES

Within the context of the issues discussed above, it is possible to detect a number of properties within the CHAGs and their interactions. I have listed several below – they are not necessarily mutually exclusive and each group may move amongst and through them at varying times.

Forced response

As long as community consultation was a relaxed and advisory process the health board could maintain control. However, national expectations and requirements for consultation mean that the board must be concerned about the composition of the CHAG and develop transparent and overt means of dealing with opinion channelled through it. For the CHAGs themselves, their freedom of action is now somewhat curtailed as they are expected and required to make comment on issues which previously they may have chosen to ignore. Equally, therefore, they have to be clearer about their own methods of working and of liaising with other groups.

Informed leverage

As a by-product of a more formal and open relationship, it is essential that the health boards see the CHAG as a part of their organisation and make special efforts both to orient and inform CHAG members so that any leverage they exert is soundly based.

Dilution of opinions

The different history, formation, composition and interests noted above make it unlikely that CHAGs will unite and speak with one voice on very many issues. At one level this might seem 'convenient' for the board since it can avoid concerted views on particular issues. However, it underlines a diversity of opinion in various localities. How the board will respond to this wide range must be clarified and will, yet again, require the processes to be more seriously considered.

165

Local focus

The notion of 'community of interest' lacks a clearly accepted definition. In the early years populations ranged in size from the city of Hamilton with 100,000 to Raglan with 4,500. The CHAGs themselves will experience their own management problems where the population is much above 20,000 – and it would clearly be impossible to regard populations of 100,000 as truly local.

Safety valve

It is well-known internationally that public consultation on any issue allows for the discharge of pent-up concern and, in some cases, anger. It now seems clear that the communities and the public see the CHAGs as a conduit for expression of opinion in addition to other more direct, but less used mechanisms such as personal representation, petition or deputation. This may be an important function of the CHAG, though again there will be confusion as to whether advice and opinion is then to be acted on.

Allegiance to dogma

It is likely that people with strong views will be elected or find their way onto public bodies. In many cases those views may not be based on evidence or information and thus various disputes between different dogmas can arise.

The test of common sense

The Health Board wishes to receive advice and comment based on informed common sense. It is not seeking to expand its board size and find partners to help shoulder its own responsibilities. If it becomes necessary to train and educate advisory group members to a high level, we can run the risk of simply increasing the number of managers from around 14 to 200, thus over burdening the management system and making it virtually impossible to take decisions.

Perceived value

From the Health Board's point of view, it will be seeking an improvement in understanding opinion and increasing community knowledge about the management of health care. From the community's point of view, they will wish to see the CHAGs as a useful instrument of consultation. It can happen that they are seen as a further bureaucratic hurdle between the community and the health board, thus leading to the recreation of single issue groups.

CREATED TENSION

The board has deliberately created a new location for consultation and negotiation, and thus a possible domain for conflict. It is therefore essential to find appropriate processes and skills to manage consultation and conflict. Ideally, lessons can be learned from the area of conflict resolution in the industrial and international diplomacy spheres. For example, 'more and more occasions require negotiation: conflict is a growth industry. Everyone wants to participate in decisions that affects them; fewer and fewer people will accept decisions dictated by someone else.' (1)

Clearly we will have to resolve the outcome of 20 separate negotiations into some final form. A classic traditional way of doing this would be to bureaucratise it – to take members of CHAGs into other groups or to combine CHAGs into small sub groups. This type of response would fly in the face of the 'community of interest' principle which underpinned the formation of them in the first place.

Summary
(Editor)

This chapter has, briefly, indicated the importance of considering the quality of relationships in place during organisational attempts to change, or to wrestle with significant problems. I suggest through my notes and the extracts that this goes way beyond simplistic 'human relations' notions about good communication and interpersonal styles. Rather, it concerns a view of the world and a willingness really to work at relationships, build common cultures and recognise and make space for other people's rights.

As a footnote, it is interesting to note that many organisational problems are described as interpersonal or personality differences. Experience as a consultant highlights that this is rarely the reality. Rather, it can indicate a willingness to individualise and then give up, without engaging in skilled 'win-win' negotiations or other helpful processes.

---

(1) Fisher, R., Ury, W. Getting to Yes. Hutchinson Business 1981.

167

BEYOND PROVIDER DOMINANCE –
THE WAY FORWARD

FIONA HASTINGS

This conference, and these edited papers, contribute to an emerging consensus across the world that provider-led health services must give way to something different. This is despite continuing arguments about the nature of providers, and of their dominance, its roots and any subsequent malfunctioning. It is also unclear what will follow provider dominance and even less clear what processes and mechanisms will ensure the transition. However, as suggested throughout, notions of clarity may not be essential for desired change to occur. Rather, appropriate responses to specific problems and issues which present may be the only way. We may eventually conclude that the 'grand scheme' and assumed clarity of other times is a myth and that progress may always have been the actions of significant people moving in a vaguely discerned direction.

Regretfully, there are no simple answers. It is easy to demonstrate the failures of macro political change, even while recognising that it makes a contribution to altered perceptions, values and power distribution. It is easy, also, to point to systems which have fought to resist change and ended up backward, dysfunctional and wasteful. It is much harder to provide a guaranteed recipe for success. In this book I have set out some ideas presented by people who are themselves significant, powerful and experienced in the kinds of struggles which are ongoing in all healthcare systems. Many of the people represented in this book are providers. In many respects, they were united only in their interests in healthcare and health and their desire to improve those processes and make a personal contribututution. What may be a unifying theme, and one which as a consultant and trainer I see in many professions and organisations, is the belief in ownership of process. The idea of a far distant 'them' who would provide solutions and answers and/or who had to be resisted at all costs has given way to a recognition that complex systems are muddled, confused and often impenetrable. The only way to improve them is to engage rather than to create a fantasy world which is not so – and then create policies and plans for that fantasy world.

Many people have written throughout history of cycles of human endeavour – large scale agricultural, industrial and political revolutions, wars, inventions and changes in societal assumptions. As this century nears its end, it is seductive to make comparisons with the last one to contemplate changes in assumptions, feelings, ideologies and processes. As

168

discussed earlier in this book, this process often demonstrates as much about the viewer as the issue. I will happily admit to a distrust about the power of science and systems to guide the world, and about the benefits of many of our present ways. Consequently, I am likely to look for suggestions that these things are changing and that we may be stumbling towards a better future.

Whatever the grand scheme of things, I hope that many people in Health Services will recognise that small scale change, personal involvement and acceptance of responsibility, some creativity, imagination, and friendliness are likely to make things better, and unlikely to make things worse. So far, a better idea eludes us.